THE TRUTH
ABOUT
Challenger

For Louis Bottoms,

The future of NASA
includes your ideas.
Let congress know your
ideas for NASA!

Randy Avera
June 2003

THE TRUTH
ABOUT
Challenger

Randy Avera

First Edition
First Printing

Special Edition-January 28, 2003
(The Centennial Year of First Flight)

RANDOLPH PUBLISHING
"Amazing stories about people and our Universe"

P. O. Box 160
Good Hope, Georgia   30641
USA
www.RandolphPublishing.com

9/4/15

THE TRUTH
ABOUT
Challenger

Randy Avera

Published by:
RANDOLPH PUBLISHING
P. O. Box 160
Good Hope, Georgia   30641, USA
Book Orders: www.RandolphPublishing.com

TECHNICAL EDITOR: Mr. Randy Avera, NASA Engineer

LAYOUT TECHNICIAN: Mrs. Rita Pleimann

ISBN, print ed., 1-932258-00-0
First Edition
First Printing, January 2003 (The Centennial Year of First Flight)

LIBRARY OF CONGRESS CATALOGING-IN PUBLICATION DATA
2002095763
Avera, Randy
The Truth About *Challenger*/Randy Avera
First Edition, First Printing

**ATTENTION CORPORATIONS, UNIVERSITIES,
COLLEGES, GOVERNMENT AGENCIES, AND
PROFESSIONAL ORGANIZATIONS:**
Quantity discounts are available for bulk purchases of this book
for educational and training purposes. Speaking engagements,
Program Management Training Programs and Workshops are
available for managers and workers. Please contact Randolph
Publishing
   www.RandolphPublishing.com

Printed in The United States of America by:
McNaughton & Gunn, Inc., on acid-free paper.

CONTENTS

DEDICATION

To Dick Scobee ("Scobes"), Commander of the last flight of Space Shuttle *Challenger* and the 51-L Mission. Commander Scobee, as my mentor, suggested that I apply to NASA as a Mission Specialist Astronaut candidate in 1983. I will forever appreciate Scobes for his encouragement, faith in me, and for the times when we shared our mutual views of the Universe.

To the relatives of the *Challenger* Astronauts, I miss the 51-L Mission Astronauts, too. The NASA team loved and admired them all.

To John Young, Chief Astronaut of the Space Shuttle Program (1973-1987), who was the first Commander to fly the Space Shuttle. On January 28, 1986, John was the pilot of the NASA G-II safety chase plane called the Shuttle Training Aircraft (STA). John Young flew safety chase for the *Challenger* 51-L mission, and was in close proximity to *Challenger* when the Shuttle breakup occurred. Perhaps no other person has worked so hard, told the space exploration story like it is, and believed so literally in the ability of Mankind to travel routinely in space. John, you're a genuine aviator and Astronaut. Your flight as Commander of the first Space Shuttle flight, STS-1 *Columbia*, was the bravest thing I have ever seen a man do.

To my mother, Clara Jo Lee Avera, who was my best friend and spiritual example. She supported me when I was learning to fly in high school, encouraged me during my college days at Georgia Tech, and enjoyed witnessing many of the amazing experiences while I worked at NASA.

To everyone, who remembers where they were on that day, January 28, 1986, when the world was shocked and grieved for what had come to pass to the *Challenger* Astronauts and to the American Space Program.

ACKNOWLEDGEMENTS

The National Aeronautics and Space Administration (NASA) was the most rewarding and creative employer that I have ever had. I sustain the utmost respect, appreciation, thanksgiving, and humility to have been selected by that federal agency to work as an engineer for the Space Shuttle Program. The NASA organization, its people, and the faithful supporters of NASA – the American taxpayers and people from around the world – have been the greatest combination that can be expected in this life.

The *William P. Rogers Presidential Commission on the Challenger Accident Investigation* that was established in 1986 by U.S. President Ronald Reagan consisted of a remarkable staff of American citizens, heroes to us all in many ways. The *Challenger* crash investigation was conducted in the last remaining years of life on Earth before sophisticated and efficient labor saving machines such as personal computers and scanners were in common use. Any mistakes, errors or false conclusions that were made or reported by the *Rogers Presidential Commission* were of human error in their nature and not intentional to history or to the people of the United States of America.

The contents of this book are true to the author's knowledge, research, and experiences and are in no manner intended to disrespect the *Rogers Presidential Commission,* The President of The United States of America, the families of the Astronauts, the citizens of the United States, or cultures from around the world. This book honors the character of humanity within people who have overcome problems of life by utilizing science and exploration to educate and heal others with compassion and service.

America has been blessed and is fortunate to have such awe-inspiring people in support of historic national programs such as the Space Shuttle Program.

INTRODUCTION

This is the story about the crash investigation of the Space Shuttle *Challenger*. It is *not* a condemnation of NASA or the space agency's contractors. Rather, it is a testimony to the exceptional qualities and practices of the organizations and leaders that have produced successful and historic program management, an exploration of ways in which management failed, and a description of the standards of excellence needed for successful aerospace research and implementation. This book had to be written in order to restore the technical accuracy of the cause of the *Challenger* crash, and to honor the unselfish and reliable working people who made great space exploration projects successful but who were rarely recognized. My primary goal in writing this book is to offer a first-person message of hope, history, and motivation to the working class of people, managers, and to the great explorers of today and of the future.

This story takes you closer to knowing the NASA and contractor employees who have been the producers of the American Space Program, and uses my experiences and research to reveal the "truth" about *Challenger*. It documents the history of the behind-the-scenes events that occurred during the emotional weeks immediately before and after the last flight of the Space Shuttle *Challenger*, and tells what it was like as NASA attempted the Return To Flight of the Space Shuttle Program with the 26th Shuttle flight of Space Shuttle *Discovery*. Was there a cover-up of the findings during the crash investigation? Did former U.S. President Ronald Reagan and his administration pressure NASA into launching an unsafe Space Shuttle

Challenger? What meaning does the *Challenger* Tragedy offer to future explorers of the Universe?

That last flight of Space Shuttle *Challenger*, identified by NASA as the *51-L Mission*, began with 71 seconds of elation and fulfillment for the Astronauts who flew aboard it and for supporters of NASA who watched the launch. *Challenger* then broke apart in flight and was destroyed within the next two seconds. After those first 73 seconds, the last 2 minutes and 26 seconds of ballistic ascent and freefall flight were nightmarish, beyond our control, horrifying, and sorrowful. Finally, *Challenger* crashed into the Atlantic Ocean. We all wanted to see Astronauts safe on parachutes, but there were none. We all wanted to see the shimmering white and black Shuttle Orbiter emerge through the chaos of debris that rained down into the Atlantic Ocean waters. But the Orbiter *Challenger* no longer existed. The spectators at the launch continued to stare into the cold, morning Florida sky, scanning the expanding cloud of cryogenic oxygen and explosive hydrogen liquids that had spilled from inside the Space Shuttle. Spectators witnessed the two Solid Rocket Boosters from *Challenger* break free and thunder aimlessly through the edge of space in the uppermost portion of the atmosphere, wandering just ahead of the Astronauts, who just moments before, were being propelled by those renegade boosters.

Challenger had left the Earth in a blaze of sunshine. It seemed to penetrate a surrealistic membrane in the sky on a one-way trajectory to the history of space exploration. NASA's attempt on that day to boost men and women into space failed into shattered elements of human endeavors, pieces of a spaceship that came to rest upon the ocean floor in the Atlantic Ocean's Gulf Stream currents.

This is my account of *Challenger*'s history and her last flight. My regular job at NASA Kennedy Space Center was Lead Engineer for Space Shuttle Orbiter structures systems engineering. In 1986, my assignment was to work the structural Breakup Analysis and Reconstruction of the *Challenger* wreckage. The day after the crash, I was assigned to a team that investigated and documented the Structural Breakup Sequence and Analysis of the Space Shuttle Orbiter. The analysis included the *Challenger's* Crew Module, fuselage, wings, engine compartment, and the 51-L mission payload, or cargo.

What is 'the truth about *Challenger?*' What really transpired behind the scenes during the accident investigation? *Challenger*'s last flight, Mission 51-L, was poorly reported by some and poorly recalled by others. As unbelievable as it may sound, even many NASA employees seem to have difficulty remembering the exact cause of the crash of *Challenger*. It is time to set the record straight.

Most people think that the "O-rings" that were nested inside the segment joints of the Solid Rocket Boosters (SRBs) were the culprit that destroyed *Challenger*. News reporters led the public to believe that the O-rings failed and caused the crash. Most people do not know or understand the great difference between the *failure* and the *malfunction* of the Space Shuttle Solid Rocket Booster design, and the catastrophic effects of those modes upon the Space Shuttle's flight. By 1977, NASA engineers in Huntsville, Alabama had already identified design and performance problems with the steel casing of the solid rocket boosters. These problems had been known for at least four years prior to the first flight of the Space Shuttle *Columbia* on April 12, 1981, but were never corrected.

Had those boosters been redesigned, I believe it would have prevented the structural breakup of *Challenger*.

Let's go back to December 1985, starting with the all-time record number of countdowns for one Shuttle launch, Space Shuttle *Columbia's* mission 61-C. Then we will progress forward only six weeks to January 28, 1986. All of us were changed on that tragic morning when we lost our Astronaut friends and heroes, and lost an old friend that we rocket engineers knew so well, the Space Shuttle Orbiter, *Challenger*.

As I began to write this story in January 1995, in Marietta, Georgia, I realized that nine years had passed since *Challenger* was destroyed. The relativity of the years seems unreal. Wasn't the launch only yesterday, or was it ten thousand years ago?

Our Astronaut heroes and colleagues, Dick Scobee, Mike Smith, El Onizuka, Judy Resnik, Ron McNair, Greg Jarvis, and Christa McAuliffe chose a lifestyle that made them the subjects and verbs of history. They became variables in the equation of their futures that included the crash of *Challenger*. From the moment that they were selected by NASA, *Challenger's* Commander Dick Scobee and his crewmembers accepted their places in history with bravery and with meaning. The Astronauts knew the general and practical sense risks of flying aboard a Space Shuttle, and they accepted those risks.

One day in 1979, just seven years before he was killed aboard *Challenger*, Commander Scobee and I worked together on a stage at Kennedy Space Center when we presented a motivational talk about the Space Shuttle Program to a group of high school students. Scobee said, "Prepare yourselves for the future and be exactly who and what you are inside your heart and mind. Don't try to become just an Astronaut. Be yourself and be pleased in that."

Scobee described to those students his prediction of what a Space Shuttle launch would be like. The Space Shuttle would not fly until two years later. He said, "These are the most powerful boosters ever built," describing them as "bad boys" in reference to their immense thrust and horsepower. There we were, an aerospace engineer and an Astronaut, attempting to inspire those students and teach them to appreciate history. "Scobes" understood the meaning of history.

Sometimes life takes us suddenly to the very front of history in the making, whether we are willing or simply a victim. That is what happened to my colleagues, friends, and heroes of the *Challenger* Astronaut Crew. The Astronauts were willing to accept the risks and hazards of Space Shuttle flight, but they ultimately became the victims of a failed NASA program management scheme that operated outside the parameters of the standard procedures for Space Shuttle vehicle design, development, and qualification.

The history about the last flight of *Challenger* has been secured in time. Many lessons have been learned and emotions shared during the *Challenger* 51-L period of history. Only the histories to come will show how well we make use of those lessons.

TRANSCRIPT OF *CHALLENGER* ASTRONAUT'S CONVERSATION DURING COUNTDOWN *FROM T-31 SECONDS THROUGH SPACE SHUTTLE CHALLENGER DISINTEGRATION DURING BOOST TO EARTH ORBIT. THE CONVERSATIONS ARE BETWEEN THE ASTRONAUTS AND NASA's MISSION CONTROL IN HOUSTON, TEXAS. THESE ARE THE LAST RECORDED WORDS OF THE CHALLENGER 51-L MISSION ASTRONAUTS. (Source: NASA)*

T-31 SEC.   PILOT MIKE SMITH   "OKAY."

T-30   COMMANDER DICK SCOBEE   "Thirty seconds down there."

T-25   SMITH   "Remember the red button when you make roll call."

T-23   SCOBEE   "I won't do that. Thanks a lot."

T-15   SCOBEE   "Fifteen."

T-6 (ORBITER 3 ENGINES IGNITE)   SCOBEE   "There they go, guys."

T-6   JUDY RESNIK (MISSION SPECIALIST)   "All right."

T-6   SCOBEE   "Three at a hundred."

T-0 (LIFTOFF)   RESNIK   "All right!"

T+1 SEC.   SMITH   "Here we go!"

T+7 (SHUTTLE CLEARS LAUNCH TOWER)

SCOBEE   "Houston, *Challenger*, roll program."

T+11   SMITH   "Go you _ _ _ _ _ _!"

T+14   RESNIK   "LVLH."

T+15   RESNIK   "_ _ _ _ hot!"

T+16   SCOBEE   "Oooh kaay."

T+19   SMITH   "Looks like we've got a lot of wind up here today."

T+20   SCOBEE   "Yea."

T+22   SCOBEE   "It's a little hard to see out my window here."

T+28   SMITH   "There's ten thousand feet and mach point five."

T+35   SCOBEE   "Point nine."

T+40   SMITH   "There's mach one."

T+41   SCOBEE   "Going through nineteen thousand."

T+43	SCOBEE	"OK, we're throttling down."
T+58	SMITH	"Throttle up."
T+59	SCOBEE	"Roger."
T+1:02	SMITH	"Thirty-five thousand. Going through one point five."
T+1:05	SCOBEE	"Reading 486 on mine."
T+1:07	SMITH	"Yep. That's what I've got, too."
T+1:10	SCOBEE	"Roger, GO at throttle up."
T+1:13	SMITH	"Uh...oh!"

The Space Shuttle *Challenger* was destroyed at that moment during its climb to Earth orbit at a speed of approximately 1,700 miles per hour and an altitude of approximately 43,500 feet.

CHAPTER 1

AMERICA'S SPACE SHUTTLE: THE ICON OF SPACE FLIGHT WORLD RECORDS

The year was 1972. The X-15 rocket plane had made its last flight several years before on October 24, 1968. The *Apollo* Program to the Moon had been terminated at the pinnacle of the Program's success. The awe-inspiring decade of the 1960s was over. The Vietnam War was ending for America. Eager for new vitality in space exploration, NASA sought to develop an American space station that would orbit Earth and a Space Shuttle rocketship to service the newly proposed U.S. space station.

The United States was making final preparations for an Earth-orbiting space station called *Skylab* that would be launched into Earth orbit on May 14, 1973. However, the new long-range NASA plans called for a more sophisticated and accommodating space station to replace *Skylab*. Astronaut John Young was the Astronaut Commander of the *Apollo* 16 Mission to the Moon and he was actually walking on the Moon in the year 1972 as the U.S. Congress approved the NASA budget to include the Space Shuttle funding. From the Moon, Young said to the people of Earth, "America needs that Shuttle mighty bad." His words carried all the way back to Earth with an uncommon authority.

There were many technological problems in the way of achieving the reality of a Space Shuttle to serve the space station. Overcoming those problems was dangerous, risky, and expensive, but the people of

NASA and the contracted workers produced the inventions and solutions for success.

Before the launch of the Space Shuttle *Columbia*, no human had ever traveled in a real spaceship. The Space Shuttle was the first. A spaceship is defined as a spacecraft in which people live, work, sleep, and travel on a reusable basis. Many achievements in engineering, science, and manufacturing did not occur until the Space Shuttle Program precipitated those accomplishments.

Mankind had never before traveled at the relative speed of Mach 25 (25 times the speed of sound in air) in a winged vehicle, and then, at later dates, flown in that same used spaceship again and again. Mach 25 flight of a Shuttle was an astounding achievement. The Space Shuttle Program developed the largest, most powerful solid rocket boosters in history, the most powerful liquid hydrogen/oxygen high-pressure "boot strap" engines, and the most advanced computer and software engineering ever flown in a manned spacecraft.

The Space Shuttle designs incorporated many new technologies that had evolved from the late 1960s and the early 1970s. Every designer, mechanic, quality inspector, and machinist who worked in the Shuttle Program realized that we were working on a program that was important to everyone in the world and that our performance would determine the Space Shuttle's future. The commitments of the employees to quality and exactness provided a safer beginning to the Space Shuttle Program and reduced the chances of malfunctions or failures that could be the demise of the program. The Space Shuttle design goals included the capability of flying seven Astronauts, plus a cargo (or payload) of up to 65,000 pounds, an altitude of up to

350 miles above the Earth, and a maximum on-orbit stay time of sixteen days.

The Space Shuttle design includes the largest glass windows ever flown into space, a full-sized toilet (technically called the Waste Containment System), many storage lockers, bed bunks, and a huge airlock for two Astronauts to prepare for their spacewalks. The airlock is an aluminum cylinder large enough to contain two people and is primarily used to prevent a physiological condition known as "the bends" when nitrogen gas bubbles form in the blood due to decompression. The second purpose for the airlock is to avoid dumping the Crew Module cabin pressure and breathing air overboard when spacewalks are necessary. The *Gemini* and *Apollo* spacecraft capsules required total decompression of the air and pressure in the "cockpit" in order for an Astronaut to go outside the spacecraft into the vacuum of space. The airlock system of the Space Shuttle orbiter avoids such troublesome and dangerous decompression procedures.

The Space Shuttle has the largest number of reaction control jets flown for attitude control of the Shuttle in orbit. The Space Shuttle incorporated the first robotic electromechanical/optical arm for handling payloads in and out of the payload bay, orbiter inspections, and video photography. Highly accessible for maintenance and inspections, the Orbiter systems and structures made it possible to fly the Space Shuttles frequently, with repeatable confidence in safe function and reliability.

On the orbiter exterior, there is also the reusable insulation tile and quilted thermal blanket system, which protects the skins and structural frame of the orbiter from melting during the hot flight into orbit from launch, and during reentry through the Earth's atmosphere. One must see this system to grasp the scope of it. The reusable tile system designers at Lockheed and NASA, the tile installers, repair technicians, and quality inspectors are the artists and sculptors of the orbiter's thermal protection system. Their excellent works saved the Space Shuttle from becoming a melted meteorite during any launch or reentry.

The mountain of paperwork for thousands of tiles and many square yards of white, quilt-like insulation blankets is incredible. Installing and repairing the Orbiter's Thermal Protection System insulation is back-breaking work. That endless effort allows the Space Shuttle to fly up through the atmosphere and later to return and fly through the atmosphere, without melting the orbiter and the Astronauts. None of these technological inventions had ever been flown on a manned spacecraft before the Space Shuttle.

The unsuccessful events of the space program can overshadow the wonderful discoveries that have been made. The successes that we have had at NASA will always bring exuberance to those of us who poured our hearts and souls into the project, the mission, and the team. Those successes are measured most accurately by the lives of those whose energy and tenacious work ethics made the space exploration "magic" happen. All of the toil, frustration, exasperation, and tears were the catalysts to the successes of the Space Shuttle Program.

This book could not begin without the respectful acknowledgment of the results of the financial investments and relentless work of everyone involved in the Space Shuttle Program. Those of us who worked directly with Space Shuttle vehicle construction, testing, processing, launching, and landing recovery invested many long hours-typically ten or fourteen hours per day. Because of our understanding of the importance of the Space Shuttle and our commitments to the work schedule, we missed many important family events as we gave priority and sacrifice to the Space Shuttle development and needs. Although I will not elaborate on the staggering number of product and invention spin-offs that have resulted from the Space Shuttle development, I will say that the Space Shuttle Program has produced a plethora of technical achievements that commenced with the first Shuttle Program launch on April 12, 1981, the first launch of Space Shuttle *Columbia*.

On that historic day, as *Columbia* was lifting off launch Pad 39A in Florida, 2,300 miles away in Palmdale, California there sat an aluminum structure that very accurately represented the structure of a real, flight-qualified Space Shuttle Orbiter. That structure was sitting there in Rockwell International's Orbiter assembly hangar where the Space Shuttle Orbiter *Columbia* had been assembled and tested. That Orbiter structure simulator was the official "structural fit-check" device called the *Structural Test Article, STA-099.*

The purpose of the *STA-099* was to verify that structures and systems for the production Orbiters would fit properly in accordance with all design drawings and specifications when finally installed into the Orbiter being constructed. The components that had "misfits" were documented so that engineering and quality control groups could solve the misfit problems before the systems were installed into the real Orbiter.

That structural test article, *STA-099,* was the airframe skeleton that after much repair and rework was renamed: Space Shuttle *Challenger*. Amazing, isn't it? NASA never imagined that the second Space Shuttle would begin as the well-used *Structural Test Article, STA-099*. U.S. President Nixon's Administration and the U.S. Congress reduced funding to the Space Shuttle Program in the early 1970s and forced the cancellation of three of the planned six Orbiters for the Shuttle Program. The only way that NASA could have the fourth Orbiter was to inspect, repair, and upgrade the *Structural Test Article, STA-099*, to a fully flight-qualified Orbiter. *STA-099* was transformed to become our old friend, *Challenger*, and she was destined to demonstrate herself to be as capable as *Columbia*. Those initial flights of *Challenger* became waypoints of time that led to the historical event that would prompt most people to recall exactly what they were doing and where they were when the history of *Challenger's* flights tragically ended on January 28, 1986.

CHAPTER 2

THE *Columbia* LAUNCH BEFORE *Challenger*

December of 1985 was a grueling month for NASA and contractor personnel at Kennedy Space Center, Florida. The pressure to launch the Shuttle was *on*. Space Shuttle *Columbia* was poised on launch Pad A at Complex 39 as the NASA launch team conducted the countdown. U.S. Congressman Bill Nelson, Democrat of Florida and Chairman of the House of Representatives Space Subcommittee of the Science, Space, and Technology Committee, was onboard Shuttle *Columbia* and became the second American elected politician to become an Astronaut. At the time, many Space Center employees talked about how outrageous and disheartening it was that elected politicians had influenced NASA to get flights aboard the Space Shuttle.

NASA employees were certain that "kicking politicians off the planet" was a wonderful idea in a comedic sense, but in a practical sense it displayed the appearance of impropriety and abuse of political powers for self-interest. If "politician boosting to orbit" was required to ensure space exploration funding, then many space workers felt that government-funded exploration was not worth it. There are so many people who were more deserving of a flight into space, such as those who helped build the Space Shuttle Program with sweat and sacrifice, or taxpayers who financed the program. It was so disappointing to the NASA Team to see elected politicians flying for free.

The NASA team felt that the politicians were taking advantage of the team and the taxpayers.

The newspapers that serve the KSC area in Brevard, Volousia, and Orange counties published articles critical of Congressman Nelson for boondoggling his way aboard the 24th Space Shuttle flight. Published in February 1986 after the *Challenger* accident, those articles were highly critical of Congressman Nelson for "bumping" Astronaut Mission Specialist, Greg Jarvis, from the *Columbia* flight, called 61-C, to the ill-fated *Challenger* flight, 51-L.

There is a crucially important story about the *Columbia* pre-launch preparations that ultimately produced a successful 24th Shuttle Mission. That Mission was the first where many NASA engineers truly became frightened about the pressures to meet the launch schedule if that meant waiving or deferring maintenance and modification requirements to do so.

I was one of two NASA engineers responsible for moving, or towing, the Orbiter *Columbia* from the Orbiter Processing Facility (OPF) to the Vehicle Assembly Building (VAB) for vertical mating (or stacking) to the External Fuel Tank and Solid Rocket Boosters. The Orbiter towing operation requires a perfect procedure, reliable ground support equipment, and trained personnel with quick reflexes. If the Orbiter were to collide with a building while being towed, the damage to the Orbiter could be financially and operationally catastrophic to the Shuttle Program.

That particular night in 1985, I was working in the Orbiter Processing Facility (OPF) Bay No. 2 as part of the Orbiter Move Team. We prepared to push back the 180,000 pound Orbiter with the T-500 tow tractor and tow bar. The magnificent black and white Orbiter was ready to emerge from the OPF hangar-like a butterfly from its cocoon.

I was overwhelmed with uncertainty about the quality and safety of the *Columbia* for that flight. We NASA engineers at KSC were aware that the subsystem managers at Johnson Space Center (JSC) had signed several hundred waivers against this particular Orbiter and mission. The waivers either eliminated or delayed mandatory requirements and maintenance items for the *Columbia*. The maintenance requirements for Orbiter processing are itemized in a very large document, or "bible," called the Orbiter Maintenance Requirements and Specification Document (OMRSD). The design of the Orbiter and the intricate subsystems require a tremendous amount of testing and maintenance between missions. Most of those maintenance requirements are accomplished in the OPF in the horizontal position for the Orbiter. The remaining OMRSD requirements for that mission are accomplished in the vertical position after vehicle stacking of the Orbiter in the Vehicle Assembly Building and after the vehicle rollout to the launch Pad.

Under normal circumstances, if any NASA engineer had asked for a waiver to a single OMRSD requirement, it would have taken a convincing sales job, almost an "act of Congress," and the alignment of all nine planets to be successful at securing management's approval for a single OMRSD waiver. Granting an OMRSD waiver required a plethora of engineering background data.

NASA management was either under pressure from federal officials in Washington, DC, or simply acted from their own fears, and waived hundreds of OMRSD requirements for that flight. NASA management acted as if those vehicle tests and launch processing requirements for the Space Shuttle and the payload were unnecessary.

In the OPF, as the tow tractor cranked up and the Operations group gave the "go ahead" to push the Orbiter *Columbia* out of the OPF, ominous thoughts came over me and my engineering colleagues.

We engineers and technicians shared feelings of disgust to roll out an Orbiter that was not processed in accordance with all requirements.   NASA and the Shuttle Program contractors did not completely ignore all safety-of-flight requirements, but the waiving of hundreds of Shuttle processing requirements was a risky disregard for the safety of the Astronauts and the Shuttle Program.   As the Orbiter *Columbia* inched backwards and rolled out of the hangar, we agreed that this Orbiter vehicle's processing time cutbacks, and waivers against engineering requirements, had resulted in an unacceptable and perhaps unsafe vehicle for a manned launch.   We were afraid.   Using waivers to compensate for not performing required maintenance is the cowardly method of flying a spaceship.   The use of waivers to accelerate the schedule was not an authorized NASA procedure.

The engineers, mechanics, and inspectors were always meticulous in Orbiter processing work.   It was disheartening and sickening when NASA upper management buckled under the pressures for meeting the launch schedule and resorted to using waivers to achieve the shortened schedule.   One danger in waiving so many vehicle requirements for the schedule is that many people lost respect for the value of the vehicle processing requirements.   Low morale and lack of respect for the official and proven NASA process of spacecraft processing is not good for assuring a safe-to-fly Space Shuttle.

As the tail of the Orbiter *Columbia* passed through the doorway of the OPF Bay 2 into the darkness of the outdoors, I said to my NASA colleague, John Fraley, "Well John, there goes the most unsafe spacecraft we have ever processed here at KSC." John profanely concurred.

The KSC Shuttle processing team had been very ambitious during vehicle processing to follow the procedures, step-by-step, according to what was agreed upon in advance by engineering. Deviations from that ethical work concept were unacceptable.

With trepidation, *Columbia* was moved another step closer to the launch that would fly Congressman Nelson, the other Astronauts of Mission 61-C, and the payloads into Earth orbit.

There were seven launch countdowns for *Columbia* 61-C (six "scrubs" and one launch) that took place between December 1985 and January 1986. A launch "scrub" is when the launch countdown is terminated due to problems with the Space Shuttle or ground equipment, or possibly environmental conditions such as weather constraints. A scrub simply means that the launch attempt for that day is over, and that NASA will try again when the problems are solved.

NASA attempted launch countdown number six with a weather forecast of 100% chance of rain. That attempt ended in a $25,000,000 scrub. There were obvious intentions to get *Columbia* launched in order to ensure that the Congressman would be satisfied with his flight. There was a prevailing sense of pressure to get on with the next Shuttle launch of *Challenger*, Mission 51-L, with the schoolteacher aboard. The 1986 *State of the Union Address to the Nation* by U.S. President Ronald Reagan was only a few days away.

Those launch attempts of *Columbia* Mission 61-C (STS-24) occurred at KSC Launch Complex 39, Pad A. Just a mile or so away on Pad B, there was Space

Shuttle *Challenger*, majestically poised and pointed towards space, complete with the now famous defective and unsafe Solid Rocket Booster joints that became the focus of the world's attention only days later.

In January 1986, I was in the Launch Control Complex (LCC) after launch scrub number four of *Columbia's* Mission 61-C. Later that afternoon, after that particular scrub, the *Challenger* 51-L Crew was at Pad B participating in rehearsals for their launch. I will never forget the looks on the faces of the *Challenger* 51-L Astronauts as they witnessed and absorbed the frustration and fears associated with the serial scrubs at Pad A of the *Columbia* 61-C Mission.

A general feeling of foreboding seemed to originate from everyone's concern that *Columbia's* problems might be duplicated aboard the *Challenger* vehicle, threatening its safety of flight. After *Columbia's* fourth or fifth scrub, we began to wonder when the lack of success would end. NASA management was considering delaying the *Columbia* Mission until after the *Challenger* 51-L Mission launch could be accomplished. However, that option was never implemented.

During one of the countdowns of *Columbia's* Mission 61-C, it was my turn to take a break from the control console located in the Engineering Support Area (ESA) that was a dedicated room on the third floor of the Launch Control Complex (LCC) just behind the Firing Room. The ESA was provided so that backup engineers and managers could be an active and a passive part of the countdown without being in the Firing Room where seats were limited.

I rode the elevator from the Firing Room down to the first floor to get coffee. I saw two Astronauts, El Onizuka and Ron McNair, who were assigned to the

Challenger 51-L Mission and had been at KSC for the launch rehearsal at Pad B during December, 1985 and January, 1986. The three of us shook hands and had small talk about how busy everyone was and how fatigued the launch team and Astronauts had become.

I can recall Ron McNair's very weak and cold handshake. El Onizuka's was stronger, but not by much. Ron had a characteristic stiff neck and back posture, but at this moment he appeared to be in a relaxed mood. El was smiling with his eyes, as he often did. We talked about the rehearsal for their upcoming launch of Mission 51-L. I asked them how the launch rehearsal was proceeding. El said, "We're not having any trouble. Nothing like the problems happening with *Columbia*."

I asked, "What's it like to be on a mission in which a *Teacher-In-Space* candidate is involved? I realize that the Press coverage more thoroughly addresses the teacher and politics than the scientific ventures of the Mission." Both Astronauts indicated that the skewed Press coverage did not hinder them. But I could sense that they were not relating their total feelings on the matter, but rather the compliance to their training.

A sixth launch attempt was made and once again, *Columbia* remained on the launch Pad. The launch team was exhausted, the Astronauts were saturated with a sense of deja vu, and the loyal spectators were running out of time and vacation money. On launch countdown number seven, *Columbia* thundered off Pad 39A into Earth orbit. The launch attempts of *Columbia* Mission 61-C were as follows:

Columbia's COUNTDOWNS FOR MISSION 61-C
No. 1. More time needed to close-out engines.
No. 2. High readings from SRB hydraulics turbine.

No. 3. Liquid oxygen fill and drain valve
problem.

No. 4. Unfavorable weather conditions.

No. 5. Obstruction in Engine #2 Oxygen
prevalve.

No. 6. Forecast of heavy rains at launch site.

No. 7. *Columbia* was finally launched.

It is clear that NASA and contractor personnel worked extremely long hours and coped with many varied engineering and technical problems associated with launching *Columbia*.

The *Columbia* launch had become a scheduling and planning nightmare for NASA in Washington, DC. Other government agency plans that were coordinated with NASA launch schedules were becoming strained. President Reagan's plans and draft of the 1986 *State of the Union Address* were nearing completion. *Challenger's* launch date was scheduled for January 26, 1986.

NASA planning meetings had become very schedule-oriented. Never before had the engineers, quality inspectors, and safety engineers been denied the opportunity to submit inputs of work items on the NASA 72-hour work schedule to accomplish necessary Shuttle processing work. Remember, there were hundreds of maintenance waivers that had already been approved by the NASA JSC, the Space Shuttle design center.

When *Columbia* finally thundered off Pad A at Launch Complex 39 at KSC, Congressman Nelson got his ride and officially became an Astronaut. That early morning launch of *Columbia* 61-C was one of the most beautiful launches ever. The sky was a deep cobalt blue just before the sun rose. The Shuttle glimmered in flight, and the rocket exhausts and plume were dramatic, as if they were stars that had cut an opening through the sky to allow entry of the Shuttle and the Astronauts into space. The Solid Rocket Booster (SRB) exhaust smoke trail traced a reminder of where the *Columbia* had just flown and how much progress had been made into the ascent profile to orbit.

The SRB exhaust smoke blocked the high-altitude, early morning sun rays and cast a great shadow to the west of the launch site, creating an illusion in the sky of a deep translucent indigo veil, or curtain, to the left of the SRB smoke trail.

Imagine a vertical column of dense white SRB smoke with the Shuttle at the top-end of that smoke column. To the left of the smoke was the indigo veil, or curtain. To the right of the smoke was the cobalt blue early morning sky. Such a beautiful, stunning launch is always a reward that seems to make the engineering battles and politics of a space launch worth the effort.

After about one minute or so into flight, *Columbia* had passed through the point in the ascent trajectory called *Max-Q* where the aerodynamic forces were the greatest on the vehicle structure. After passing through *Max-Q*, *Columbia's* three Space Shuttle Main Engines (SSMEs) had increased their thrust levels to the targeted thrust values for that early portion of the launch ascent into orbit. *Columbia* was thundering into orbit as the Astronauts on board realized the unique thrills of leaving the planet for a while. That launch was the last peaceful launch in which the launch team and the world of spectators would not tense up when the Shuttle Commander calls, "GO AT THROTTLE-UP." The tension would develop from concern that any Shuttle could structurally break apart at 71 seconds into flight, which is what would happen a few days later to *Challenger*.

The launch team was relieved that the *Columbia* vehicle processing and launch to Earth orbit was over, as far as KSC's mission responsibility was concerned. After a traditional NASA launch party and a very much-needed night of rest, we would focus all of our attention on the countdown and launch of the *Challenger* 51-L Mission. As history has recorded, NASA's lack of launch success did not end with the six scrubs and the eventual launch of *Columbia* in January, 1986. Only sixteen days later, the greatest setback of NASA's programs would play out like a nightmare–that of the *Challenger* Tragedy on January 28, 1986.

Chapter 3

Challenger's 51-L Mission:
First Countdown

Columbia's grueling seven-countdown ordeal exhausted the NASA launch team. With no time for a rest, the team began focused work on *Challenger*. NASA and contractor Space Shuttle workers embarked on what would become the 25th launch of the Space Shuttle. Most of those employees, as usual, were praying for the success of the 51-L Mission Astronauts, the payload, and the Space Shuttle, for a successful flight so that we could fly that Shuttle again in the future.

The *Challenger* 51-L Mission was to place a very large NASA-owned tracking and data relay satellite called TDRS (pronounced "Tee-Drus") into Low Earth Orbit (LEO), and deploy the satellite from the Orbiter's cargo bay. That satellite was to become part of the TDRS network of several satellites already in Earth orbit, used for Space Shuttle operations and communications by processing and transmitting data, video, and voice audio.

Another 51-L Mission objective was to conduct optical observations from Low Earth Orbit of Haley's Comet. Low Earth Orbit, or LEO, refers to an orbit about Earth that is up to 350 miles high. The optical payload was stowed in tandem order in the *Challenger* Payload Bay with the TDRS satellite. The original launch date for the *Challenger* 51-L mission was January 22, 1986, but *Challenger* did not fly until January 28, 1986.

The teacher who was selected to fly on *Challenger*

51-L mission, Christa McAuliffe, was assigned to conduct class from the Orbiter during the flight as thousands of school students would have participated on Earth.   Christa, as she was affectionately called, appeared to be nervous about the hazards of the flight, but who wouldn't be?   Her expression suggesting disbelief, awe, and amazement was the same as many other Astronauts who walked up to a massive Space Shuttle vehicle that was poised on the launch Pad.

We had seen that expression on so many faces of Astronauts and visitors.   Our expressions were the same most days or nights when we drove out to the launch Pad for routine work on the Space Shuttle. Most of us rocket engineers and technicians who worked at the launch Pad could never walk to our cars at the end of our shift without stopping at least once, usually twice, to take another look at the Space Shuttle on the Pad—a sight which certainly motivates one to ponder the uniqueness and capabilities of such a useful machine.   We knew that the rocket on the Pad was an elevator to space, and it was right there before us.   Many of us who worked at the launch Pads couldn't help fantasizing about stowing away aboard the Space Shuttle.

During a Space Shuttle launch countdown, some of the engineers had duty in the Firing Room, or some-times a smaller, windowless room behind the Firing Room called the Engineering Support Area (ESA).   The Firing Rooms, located in the Launch Control Complex (LCC), were numbered FR-1, FR-2, and FR-3.   The *Challenger* 51-L Mission was controlled from FR-2.

Certain engineers at KSC were assigned to be Lead Engineers for certain missions, and they were responsible for their systems aboard the specific Orbiter that would fly the Mission.   If the Mission being launched was the Mission for which I was Lead, I was required to be on duty at the computer console in the Firing Room for countdown. I was not assigned as Lead Engineer for the 51-L Mission and had no Firing Room duty for that launch. That meant that I could be outside to watch the launch. I was excited about this because that was the first Space Shuttle launch from Pad B at Complex 39. The viewing angle was different from the previous 24 launches, so I brought my camera to take my own photos. Little did I realize that the launch just a few days later in the skies over the Cape would have such historical importance.

Even though I was not assigned as Lead Engineer for the 51-L Mission and was not required in the Firing Room for countdown, I could never stay away from the activities in the Firing Room. Imagine having total access to the Space Shuttle Firing Rooms for the countdown. I wasn't about to be anywhere else but in the middle of the action with the people and the spaceships for which I cared so much. I monitored the last hour of launch countdown progress from the ESA until the last nine minutes.

Three days before the first launch attempt, a Crew Module technician had detected a problem with *Challenger's* flight crew entry hatch that was located on the Orbiter forward fuselage area. He discovered that a screw and a nutplate on the Orbiter entry door had galled or stripped the threads. The screw and nutplate were part of an aluminum plate that had thermal tiles bonded to the plate, designed to protect the hatch from heat of reentry.

On January 27, 1986, the day of the first launch attempt of *Challenger* 51-L, the Crew Module hatch, or entry door, was closed, latched, and locked. Then the cabin pressure and relief valves were functionally tested for flight. The technicians then attempted to install the aluminum plate with tiles onto the Orbiter entry door.

At that very late point in the countdown, with the Astronauts strapped in their seats, or "closed-out" as we would say, a single screw worth only a dime galled up as it was being threaded into the nutplate. On international television, this calamity became very embarrassing and should have never occurred. The galled screw should have been properly documented and reported the day before but the technician failed to do so. The defective nutplate and screw could have been replaced on the day that it was discovered.

During the launch hold, the NASA and Lockheed management did not handle the matter well. The Orbiter Close-Out Crew at the Pad did not have a drill for drilling out the defective screw. Those events were still being broadcast on international television. We felt as if somebody should please get the shepherd's hook and get those guys off the stage. Better yet, pull the plug to *NASA Select* television network.

To add disbelief to the comedy of errors playing at the Pad, a Lockheed manager left from the LCC and drove to the Pad to try to offer his help in the structural repair matter. The manager went to the Pad because Close-Out Crew realized, on international television, that the batteries in the drill were dead. What next? We learned what next, only two days later, when *Challenger* finally was launched for the last time, on January 28. The first launch attempt was scrubbed due to time wasted on the side hatch screw repair show. The launch was scrubbed because the launch opportunity window of time had passed and weather conditions had degraded.

I went home that night and before going to sleep I read through a Space Shuttle Systems Summary book. I was always trying to learn a little bit more about that magnificent flying machine. After reviewing many pages, I set the book on my dresser. Several days after the *Challenger* crash, I picked up that same book from where I had left it on my dresser, and on the next page were the pictorials and descriptions of the Solid Rocket Booster joints and seals. Those were the parts that failed and malfunctioned, respectively, during the 51-L launch and caused the Shuttle to breakup. I was not familiar with the SRB O-ring designs until the day after the *Challenger* crash.

The *Challenger* Astronauts were disappointed that their launch countdown had been scrubbed. I am sure that the Crew wondered if that scrubbed launch was the first of many like the ones *Columbia* had experienced. Like other Astronaut crews before them who had experienced launch scrubs, the *Challenger* Astronaut pilots put the 51-L Mission delays and frustrations out of their minds by practicing Orbiter landings at KSC in the Gulfstream II *Shuttle Training Aircraft (STA)*. The Mission Specialists Astronauts kept busy by reviewing their responsibilities and procedures for the mission.

The scrubbed launch provided the opportunity for the Astronauts to talk with their families and friends one last time. Christa McAuliffe and Greg Jarvis went bike riding on State Road 3 that leads to the Vehicle Assembly Building (VAB) area from the Operations & Checkout building where the Astronauts' quarters are located. Some reporters discovered that Christa and Greg were riding bikes on the space center. The reporters followed them and conducted a rolling interview. Christa and Greg indicated that they looked forward to their launch, but they seemed uneasy.

The launch team then conducted what is called a Launch Turnaround that prepared the Shuttle and support to be reset for launch. A bookmark of time was about to be placed into the history of the world and certainly for the history of aviation and space flight.

Chapter 4

Challenger's 51-L Mission: Second and Last Countdown

If you have the feeling that the launch team and *Challenger* 51-L Astronauts had become tired and frustrated, then I have done a good job of relating the environment at KSC just a day or so before the 51-L launch.

During 1985, I said to friends and family that if the NASA management did not stop buckling under from political pressures above them, something catastrophic could happen to the Space Shuttles and the Astronauts. My family and friends said that I had been working too hard and needed a vacation. They were right about the vacation. I was also right about potential trouble with the Space Shuttles. Many of the space workers felt this way. Sometimes we got those premonitions from engineering disagreements. Sometimes those feelings developed from fatigue and schedule pressures.

I never slept very well the night before a launch. I was always too excited. There was always a magical sense in the air. I tossed and turned as I tried to convince myself that I was sleeping well. I was easily awakened by my alarm clock so I got ready for the big day that was underway. I drove to the Space Center. The only visual difference that morning was that the Space Shuttle was on Pad B instead of Pad A as we were accustomed to seeing. The wind was blowing briskly. The sky was clear, and the air was unusually cold.

For my route to work, I drove north through the Cape Canaveral Air Force Station, then west across the NASA Causeway from the Cape to the Kennedy Space Center on Merritt Island. I stopped by the Operations & Checkout building (O&C) to see the *Challenger* Astronauts leave their quarters and board the Astro-van for the ten-mile ride to Pad B. At the Pad, the *Challenger* awaited the arrival of the Astronauts and entry into the world's truly reusable spaceship. The Astro-van, as we called it, was a stainless steel, modified recreation vehicle-type design.

I parked my car in the rear parking lot of the O&C building, just south of a large heat exchanger or cooling tower that was part of the O&C air conditioning system. That cooling tower has baffles over which the air conditioning system warm water spills to chill the air conditioner water for reuse. I had my camera with me and had planned to photograph the *Challenger* Astronaut Crew as they walked out of the O&C building's famous Astronaut walkway to board the Astro-van. On July 16, 1969 the *Apollo* 11 Astronauts walked down that same walkway to board their Astro-van ride to the launch Pad that began the historic mission of the first manned landing on the Moon.

I got out of my car and noticed a beautiful, clear blue sky and the obvious cold bite in the air that set the mood for that day. The uncommonly cold weather became another factor that helps me remember so vividly what the day was like at KSC on the day that we lost the *Challenger* Astronauts, the Space Shuttle *Challenger*, and the payload.

I had not arrived early enough to see the Astronauts walk down the famous walkway. The Crew was already walking down the concrete ramp as the small crowd of well-wishers applauded and cheered for what the Astronauts expected to be one of the greatest days of their lives.

There was a definite excitement permeating the air after the crew had walked down that walkway. It was magnified with each anxious step as the Astronauts eagerly pressed on towards the "Astro-van" and then to the Pad. I could hear the spectators cheering and applauding, as the NASA security escort cars with blue lights flashing were poised, ready to guide the Astro-van to the launch Pad. The security cars were lined up on the west side of the O&C building in the cool shadow of the building. I realized that the Astronauts were already aboard the Astro-van and that the NASA security driver, a friend of mine, was ready to drive to the Pad.

As I walked towards the O&C building, I helped a woman to balance as she walked. She and I were slipping and sliding in the inch-thick ice that had formed on the asphalt of the parking lot on the driveway where the Astro-van would shortly pass by the two of us. The ice had formed there because the wind had blown the water from the cooling tower and the cold weather had frozen the water. I had my camera in my right hand as I assisted her across the ice with my left arm to balance both of us. She said, "It is *so* cold." I said, "Who would believe that you and I are ice skating in Florida? I hope all goes well for the launch." We stopped and wobbled in place on the ice because the Astro-van was now emerging from the drive between the wings of the O&C building. The Astro-van made a left turn to the south, and then a curving right turn to the west. It continued about twenty feet and passed right in front of us. As the Astro-van rolled over the ice on the driveway, the ice made a crunching sound with the front wheels, and then the same noise with the rear wheels. I took a couple of pictures with the van right in front of me. That was the last picture I could ever take of my Astronaut friends.

During the Astro-van departure to Pad B, Shuttle Commander Dick Scobee waved as the Astro-van passed by. I doubt that "Scobes" knew that I was there beside the Astro-van. In my heart I receive that wave as a parting good-bye. It was the kind of wave that symbolized how life has a momentum that sometimes is beyond all of us to define or to control. I think about that moment many times. A wave good-bye is for good luck, thanks for everything, I'll miss you, or I'll see you again. Knowing Scobes as I did, I'm sure he was meaning, "Thanks for everything. I'll see you soon." I'll never forget the sound of that ice being crushed by the Astro-van tires.

The NASA security escort, complete with a white Huey helicopter, and a Lockheed C-130 Infrared Observation aircraft flying overhead led and protected the way to the Pad. The course to the launch Pad proceeded west on the NASA Causeway, then north on the Merritt Parkway (SR 3), east on Saturn Causeway with a stop alongside the Launch Control Complex and Press Site to drop off the personnel in the Astro-van that were not required at the Pad for Crew close-out and launch operations.

As the Astro-van drove away from the O&C building, the woman and I wobbled back across the ice. She went to her office in the O&C building and I returned to my car and followed far behind the security escort to the Complex 39 area. I parked my car near the giant VAB building and went into the LCC to see how things were progressing with the count-down.

I went to the room behind the Firing Room known as the Engineering Support Area (ESA). I monitored the progress of the launch countdown and helped to troubleshoot a couple of vehicles with mechanical system issues. As the countdown progressed, I became aware that the Ice Team on Pad B was having serious concerns regarding the Pad's ability to support a launch in the icy conditions. The Ice Team is a small group composed of Engineers from various NASA centers and contractor representatives who are responsible for the engineering of the External Tank, Solid Rocket Boosters, and Thermal Protection System (TPS) insulating tiles.

The Ice Team's duty was to survey the Pad during countdown and report back to the launch management team in the LCC regarding ice buildup on the ET, SRBs, and Orbiter interfaces that could present a risk of damage to insulating tiles, windows, or flight controls. Ice damage or interference to those systems could result in catastrophe. Excessive ice buildup on the Shuttle can cause a delay or scrub a launch. Ice accumulation on the Shuttle, the launch Pad, or the launch tower would be difficult for the managers to discern from three miles away in the LCC. The 51-L Mission launch management team would learn an enormous lesson in determining severity of conditions.

The Ice Team was required to report their finding to the Launch Director in the LCC. The Ice Team's procedure called for their assessment of launch Pad and Shuttle conditions to be reported via an Operational Intercom System (OIS) communications box. But the Ice Team was unable to even hook up to the OIS box with their headsets because the boxes were covered with a thick layer of clear ice. They resorted to hand-held radios to communicate to the

Launch Director.

The Ice Team reported that a significant amount of ice had accumulated at all levels of the launch tower. The tower's various levels were constructed of metal gratings for floors. An·unwise decision had been made the day before to configure the fire suppression pipes on the launch tower to vent their water pressure during the night. The intention was to prevent the fire extinguisher water pipes on the tower from bursting due to freezing from the cold temperatures that were forecast for the night of January 27.

That spraying water was wind-blown all over the tower and the Mobile Launch Platform (MLP). The MLP is a massive, gray square volume that resembles a square steel ship about the size in area of a baseball diamond infield. The entire Shuttle vehicle sat atop the MLP for launch.

Most of the engineers and scientists in the LCC were unaware that the Pad was so encapsulated in ice. Most of the conversations between the Ice Team and the Launch Director were on channels of the hand-held radios and OIS system that did not interfere or distract from the Launch Team's focus on the procedure.

From our closed circuit television channels in the LCC, we saw the Ice Team literally shoveling ice overboard from the MLP upper surface. The MLP's water drain gutters also had to be cleared of ice. This spectacle of ice shoveling was phenomenal. The episode at the Pad definitely got the attention of the conservative Launch Team engineers in the Firing Rooms and ESA. We had never seen this problem before, and the procedures did not clearly address an icing problem of this direct magnitude. But with a *State of the Union Address* to be broadcast that night, what's a little ice?

The NASA launch management team failed in their launch decision-making process. There were many debates after the crash questioning the launch rules which required that a Space Shuttle launch should not be performed during adverse weather conditions, as determined by the Launch Team and Management Team. As the Ice Team shoveled ice overboard from the MLP, NASA managers had already made up their minds to continue the countdown. The concerns over the ice dominated the minds of the Management Team. The managers began to minimize the fact that the main reason the ice existed on the Pad was the extreme cold temperature for Florida. The launch management team talked themselves out of scrubbing the launch. The cold temperatures and the ice buildups were prohibitive safety-of-launch issues, but the Launch Director and his management team had their minds set to launch the *Challenger* on that day. Except for the adverse weather conditions, there were no unsolvable constraints to stop the launch. In fact, the delay in countdown due to icing allowed the temperature outside to increase to an acceptable value for launch. The effects of cold weather on the SRB's were not considered by the launch team.

The basic decision to continue the countdown in such adverse weather conditions was flawed, regardless of the fact that not all of the Launch Team Managers were aware that the Solid Rocket Boosters had design deficient booster segment field joints. No Shuttle should be launched in any weather condition that can degrade the safety and reliability of the Space Shuttle systems and ground systems. The Launch Team was largely unaware of the long, political, and cowardly engineering qualification history for the SRBs that had taken place from 1977 to 1980 at the Marshall

Space Flight Center in Huntsville, Alabama and at the Morton Thiokol facility in Ogden, Utah.

It must be said that the launch rules had not matured to a level that would accommodate all situations and conditions for a launch countdown.   There had been only 24 previous Space Shuttle launches by that time and NASA launch procedures would soon be completely overhauled in the days following the crash.

Mr. Gene Thomas, the NASA Launch Director for the *Challenger* 51-L launch, is a long-time colleague of mine.   I worked with Gene for fourteen years in the NASA Vehicle Engineering Directorate.   Gene finally achieved the responsible position of NASA Launch Director that he aspired to become; the *Challenger* crash would become a heartbreak for Gene personally. Gene and I faithfully shared the same church family for years at Merritt Island, Florida.   I know that Gene always tried to do the morally correct actions in his work, and the *Challenger* 51-L launch countdown was no exception.   Gene, like so many of the NASA and contractor team knew the Astronauts professionally and socially.   The loss of the Astronauts was gut-wrenching to us all.

Gene's efforts to lead the launch team to success on January 28, 1986, were thwarted by a flawed design of the SRBs and a flawed launch decision process.

On that day, January 28, 1986, there were too many latent, or undetected, faults in the SRB joints to have a safe launch.   Unfortunately, the thirty-three thousand or so parameters that were monitored on the Shuttle were indicating that all systems were performing adequately.   Overall systems status seemed good for the vehicle.   However, the SRB field joint structural stiffness design problem was about to reveal itself.   Meanwhile, the Countdown Clock was still holding at T-20 minutes.

I had been in the Engineering Support area for quite some time during this last countdown. The hold at T-20 minutes was dragging on and on. My fellow engineers and managers who were listening on their headsets had informed me that the Ice Team was having a difficult time coping with the conditions of the MLP surface. I did see on our large, overhead television monitor that the Ice Team was actually shoveling ice overboard from the water gutters at the perimeter of the MLP. That got our attention in the ESA and we concluded that we probably would not launch that morning.

My mother had traveled to my home in Cape Canaveral to visit me and to see the launch. I had arranged a car pass for her to enjoy a front row viewing spot. I began to be concerned for her being out in the cold weather unnecessarily if we were not going to launch. She decided to stay at my home instead of driving to the NASA viewing site. The skies were blue, but the wind chill factor was just too cold. I left the ESA and walked over to the empty Firing Room 1 so that I could call her and give her the status of the launch countdown. Firing Room 1 was the control room for the first Space Shuttle launch of *Columbia* in 1981. I took a seat at the Launch Director position in Firing Room 1 and used the telephone. I said to my mother, "I don't think that we're going to launch today, because of the adverse weather conditions. The countdown delay is causing us to lose the launch window." She said, "It's so cold out there. I'm not going outside until the Shuttle's up in the air. I think I'll just watch it from the front door. I hope you're not disappointed."

Just as I was telling my mother that we would

not launch, an announcement was made over the KSC public announcement system. The announcement was from the Test Conductor for the launch countdown. He said, "Attention all personnel. The countdown clock will start on my mark...three, two, one MARK. T-minus 20 minutes and counting." I couldn't believe it. I was shocked. I couldn't understand how the Test Conductor had picked up the count so soon, especially after all of the cold temperatures and ice on the launch Pad problems. My mother said, "They're not saying anything about it on the television. They're still saying its not gonna go." I said, "Then they're wrong. The reporters don't know the countdown has resumed."

I hurried back to the ESA to see what was happening and to make it real to myself that the count-down clock had really started. I grabbed my camera and headed outside to secure a prime spot for photo-graphing the first Space Shuttle launch off of Pad B. That old familiar excitement kicked in just like it had for the past 24 launches. It was the kind of emotional and physiological excitement that causes your heart to pound. The adrenaline in my body poured like rain.

I exited the LCC via the main door on the ground floor. I ran across the Saturn Causeway road and spotted a prime viewing spot on top of an office that was a converted railroad boxcar. I slung my camera over my shoulder and neck and climbed the steel ladder on the end of the white boxcar. As the countdown clock ticked toward the moment of history about to unfold, more people climbed atop the boxcar office. We had a fantastic view of the launch Pad, the Shuttle, the LCC, the VAB, and the big, blue, mid-morning skies of the Cape. The invited friends and relatives of Christa McAuliffe were seated in the bench seats in front of us. The television broadcast that would show Christa's mother and father with those facial extremes of elation, confused horror, and disbelief was broadcast from that grandstand.

There was a U.S. Air Force colonel standing next to me for the last ten minutes of the countdown. It was very cold on top of the boxcar. I was getting really excited and I felt every remaining second of the countdown like my heartbeat. I told the colonel, "This launch from Pad B will look really different."

The T-minus nine-minute mark passed, which indicated that the Ground Launch Sequencer (GLS) had taken proper control of the countdown. The GLS is a massive computer program that automatically executes the final nine minutes of countdown. The GLS is a ground-based computer program that resides in the LCC computers.

The T-minus five-minute point in the countdown had passed, and the Crew was performing the start of the Auxiliary Power Units (APUs) that are located in the Orbiter engine compartment. The APUs provide hydraulic power for the Orbiter systems.

The countdown clock continued to approach the T-31 second point where the Shuttle's onboard computer software takes command and control of the remaining seconds of the countdown. The computer transition at the T-31 second point is always a tense moment for the launch team. There is always the chance of a halt in the countdown if the Orbiter General Purpose Computers (GPCs) detect a Launch Commit Criteria violation.

The Orbiter GPCs compare actual, real-time measurements to the pre-established criteria for launch commit. If critical or essential functions of the Shuttle are out of acceptable engineering range, the GPCs will stop the countdown at the T-31 second point.

At T-31 seconds, the GLS transition to the onboard GPC computers passed like clockwork. The spectators applauded for the success of the computer transition. The countdown clock kept on ticking. We were about to have a launch. All weariness was cast aside. I began to breathe rapidly from excitement. Spectators and the launch team were all standing and were full of anticipation for the spectacle of an Earth-rattling launch.

CHAPTER 5

THE LAUNCH
AND
LAST FLIGHT
OF *Challenger*

The outdoor public address system at Kennedy Space Center was broadcasting selected portions of the live voice transmissions from the Astronauts and from the launch team at KSC and JSC. The NASA guests at the launch site and the television viewers never hear all of the conversations that are transmitted or recorded. The NASA Public Information Officer, commonly called "The Voice of NASA," provides a general commentary to the public so that more people can understand what is happening during the countdown. The Voice of NASA also provides detailed information about the flight crew's education and experience, as well as information about the goals of the Mission and the payload.

The following sequence of countdown events combines what the public normally hears during countdown broadcasts with the addition of conversations between the *Challenger* Astronauts, as it happened. These words were spoken by the NASA Public Information Officer at KSC and at JSC, the launch team Orbiter Test Conductor (OTC) from the Firing Room at KSC, and the *Challenger* 51-L Astronauts who were lying atop the rocket in the Shuttle Orbiter Crew Module at launch Pad B.

THE LAST RECORDED WORDS OF THE CHALLENGER 51-L MISSION ASTRONAUTS THAT WERE HEARD BY THE GENERAL PUBLIC ARE SHOWN HERE NEXT TO THE BOLD CREWMEMBER'S NAME. *More conversation is revealed in the Introduction of this book. Additional conversation recordings may be obtained from the NASA publication, NASA NEWS, Dated September 30, 1986, Release No: 86-137, titled, NASA Releases 51-L Pre-launch Intercom Tape Transcripts.*

T-9 MINUTES AND HOLDING...(A normal built-in hold for a Shuttle countdown.)

T-9 MIN. 15 SEC.   NASA KSC ANNOUNCER: "We are fifteen seconds away from resuming the countdown and looking at a launch of 51-L at eleven-thirty. "

T-9 MIN.   NASA KSC ANNOUNCER: "And we are at T-9 and counting.   The Ground Launch Sequencer program has been initiated."

T-5 MIN.   ORBITER   TEST   CONDUCTOR: "PLT/OTC, Perform APU start."

T-4 MIN. 57 SEC.   PILOT MIKE SMITH: "In work."

T-4 MIN.   NASA   KSC   ANNOUNCER: "T-4 minutes."

T-3 MIN. 58 SEC.   ORBITER   TEST   CONDUCTOR: "PLT/OTC, Flight crew close visors."

T-3 MIN. 30 SEC.   NASA KSC ANNOUNCER: "T minus three minutes thirty seconds and counting.   Orbiter ground support equipment service bus has been turned OFF and the vehicle is on internal power."

T-2 MIN. 44 SEC.   NASA KSC ANNOUNCER: "T minus two minutes forty-four seconds and counting."

T-2 MIN. 41 SEC.   PILOT MIKE SMITH: "OTC/PLT The Caution and Warning memory is CLEAR. No expected errors."

T-2 MINS. 20 SEC.   NASA KSC ANNOUNCER: "T minus two minutes twenty seconds…"

T-31 SEC.   NASA LAUNCH TEAM MEMBER: "We're GO for auto sequence START."

T-31 SEC   PILOT MIKE SMITH: "Okay."

T-30 SEC.   NASA KSC ANNOUNCER: "T minus thirty seconds."

T-30   COMMANDER DICK SCOBEE: "Thirty seconds down there."

T-25   SMITH: "Remember the red button when you make roll call."

T-23   SCOBEE: "I won't do that. Thanks a lot."

T-15 SEC.   NASA KSC ANNOUNCER: "T minus fifteen seconds."

T-15   SCOBEE: "Fifteen."

T-10 SEC.   NASA ANNOUNCER: "Ten, nine, eight, seven, six, we have Main Engine START…"

T-6 (ORBITER 3 ENGINES IGNITE)
SCOBEE: "There they go, guys."

T-6   JUDY RESNICK (MISSION SPECIALIST):
"All right."

T-5   SCOBEE: "Three at a hundred."

T-4 THRU T+7   NASA KSC Announcer: "...four, three, two, one and Liftoff. Liftoff of the twenty-fifth Space Shuttle Mission and it has cleared the tower."
RESNICK: "All right!"

(*Challenger* lifted off at 11:38:010 A. M. EST on January 28, 1986.)

T+1 SEC.   SMITH: "Here we go!"
T+7 (SHUTTLE CLEARS LAUNCH TOWER)
SCOBEE: "Roll program."
T+8 SEC.   CAPCOM in Houston: "Roger Roll, *Challenger*."
T+11   SMITH: "Go you _ _ _ _ _ _!"
T+14   RESNICK: "LVLH."
T+15   RESNICK: "_ _ _ _ hot!"
T+16   SCOBEE: "Oooh kaay."
T+19   SMITH: "Looks like we've got a lot of wind up here today."
T+20   SCOBEE: "Yea."
T+22   SCOBEE: "It's a little hard to see out my window here."
T+28   SMITH: "There's ten thousand feet and mach point five."
T+35   SCOBEE: "Point nine."
T+40   SMITH: "There's mach one."
T+41   SCOBEE: "Going through nineteen thousand."

T+43   SCOBEE: "OK, we're throttling down."

T+58 (ORBITER ENGINES THROTTLE UP.)
         SMITH: "Throttle up."

T+59 SEC.   SCOBEE: "Roger."

T+1MIN. 2SEC.   SMITH: "Thirty-five thousand. Going through one point five."

T+1:05   SCOBEE: "Reading 486 on mine."

T+1:07   SMITH: "Yep. That's what I've got, too."

NASA CAPCOM (CAPSULE COMMUNICATOR IN HOUSTON AT MISSION CONTROL): "*Challenger*, GO at throttle-up."

T+1:10   SCOBEE: "Roger, GO at throttle up."

T+1:13   SMITH: "Uh...oh!"

The Space Shuttle *Challenger* and the payload appeared to be instantly destroyed at that moment during the climb to Earth orbit at a speed of approximately 1,700 miles per hour and an altitude of approximately 43,500 feet.

From my vantage point, *Challenger* at ignition belched a bright white mass of fire, smoke, and steam, as the Space Shuttle appeared to silently rise from the launch Pad. The three-mile distance between the Launch Control Complex and Pad B caused a time delay of a few seconds before we could hear the engine rumble and crackle. I was taking photos as auto-wind motors from other cameras could be heard throughout the area. A few seconds after Space Shuttle Main Engine (SSME) ignition, the thunderous roar and crackle so characteristic of a Space Shuttle launch hit us like a wave. I was still taking pictures. All of the spectators seemed to be cheering, yelling, and encouraging the Space Shuttle and the 51-L Astronauts into space. Thoughts of cold weather, ice, wind, and launch delays were instantly removed from our minds.

I heard the NASA announcer on the Public Address System say the ascent profile call, "Tower Clear," indicating that the *Challenger* had climbed higher than the launch Pad tower. Next, I heard the call, "Roll Program," as called by the Commander, Dick Scobee. That call from *Challenger* was to confirm to JSC controllers in Houston, Texas that *Challenger* had responded to computer flight guidance commands of roll, pitch, and yaw to the Space Shuttle. In the rock-etry business we referred to that process as producing a State Vector for nominal Ascent Profile Major Mode 101. Major Mode 101 was the portion of ascent between ignition/first motion and burnout of the SRBs at about two minutes and twenty seconds into flight.

The purpose for this mid-air ballet maneuver is to point the Space Shuttle to the proper direction in the sky for an efficient and safe climb from the Earth into space. A second reason for this "Roll Program" maneuver is to conserve hypergolic propellants that are needed for flight control while in Earth orbit. The logic is to manipulate the exhausts that are exiting the rear of the Shuttle (SRB and SSME exhausts) to perform the Roll Program. Since that exhaust was being expended anyway, we take advantage of it in order to conserve other propellants. The Roll Program places the Orbiter in a "heads-down" attitude. Most scientific work in orbit is conducted with the Orbiter upside down toward the Earth. The Roll Program eliminates one maneuver in orbit to roll the Orbiter upside down. The JSC launch controller, the Capsule Communicator (CAPCOM), announced, "Roger, Roll Program confirmed." The *Challenger* continued to fly, as she pounded the Earth with thunderous noise, accelerating toward the heavens, higher and faster, while stresses upon the vehicle increased. I continued to look just over the top of my camera as I took more photos. I noticed a small flicker in the SRB exhaust plume, and reflexively snapped a photo. Just as the shutter in my camera released, the *Challenger* appeared to explode before my eyes.

I continued to take photos while peering over the top of the camera. What had been a magnificent black and white Space Shuttle riding atop a controlled, brilliant flame, instantly—I mean instantly—became a massive, convoluted, expanding gas ball with debris ejecting in several parabolic trajectories.

I immediately thought that the Orbiter Space Shuttle Main Engines (SSME) had failed and exploded. I imagined nothing else. It seemed certain that the Astronauts had been killed. With no escape system in the "operational" Space Shuttle, there was no way to break away from such a catastrophic event. The U.S. Air Force Colonel standing next to me said, "Maybe the Orbiter will return to the Shuttle landing strip." I said to him, "There's no way. The vehicle is destroyed." I was heartbroken.

I wanted to run to the ocean and catch the Astronauts. All we could do was watch in disbelief. After the Space Shuttle lifted off from Pad B and cleared the tower, the NASA announcer from JSC then had the responsibility of providing the commentary as *Challenger* continued to fly through the sky. The announcer continued to call the altitudes, speeds, and down-range distances of the *Challenger*, even though the *Challenger* had already been destroyed and had begun the freefall into the ocean. Hearing the announcement information was confusing to all of us spectators because the intensity of the scene of *Challenger* breaking up did not fit with the broadcast that described increasing altitudes and velocities. The Public Affairs announcer was looking head-down and was reading from a pre-arranged script, unaware that *Challenger* had broken up in flight. Unbelievable!

The two Solid Rocket Boosters had continued to fly aimlessly over the Florida skies and turned back towards the populated coast in a teasing manner. This dangerous event was very strange. The SRB exhausts formed the sketch of a scorpion, or "crab claw" design in the sky. Suddenly the SRBs stopped flying and appeared to be snuffed out. The Range Safety Officer (RSO) and the U.S. Air Force Eastern Missile Test Range Safety Officer had destroyed the boosters by radio command because the boosters were out of control. I was absorbing these events very quickly and I continued to take photos.

The Kennedy Space Center was generally quiet on the ground. A very eerie, subdued, and delayed rumble from the SRBs continued to cascade down from the heavens, even though the *Challenger* was falling like leaves and rocks into the Atlantic Ocean. This unnerving rumble gave me a false feeling that the Shuttle was still flying normally. My eyes were telling me that was impossible and my mind was telling me to disregard the rumble.

There were very long, white, vertical trails of cryogenic oxygen vapors being painted on the canvas of the blue sky. The smoke vapor trails reminded me of white crepe paper streamers. I had desperate and helpless feelings as my friends and colleagues were falling to their deaths, if they were not already dead.

The Colonel and another man pointed to the sky and said, "There's a parachute." They were hopeful that the Astronauts had parachutes and had somehow escaped the Space Shuttle breakup. I knew there were no parachutes for the Astronauts. For years we engineers had argued in vain to have an escape system in the Shuttle.

I recognized the parachute as one of the "pilot" or "drogue" chutes that is part of the SRB parachute deployment system. Amazingly, after the SRBs had been destroyed, there was a drogue or pilot chute floating safely to the Atlantic as if it were looking down on this devastating, horrible event. The small chute appeared to be circling like a buzzard. The motion of the chute was tranquil, a spot of peace in the midst of chaos. That was a very unsettling sight.

The open loop of the public address system had a small amount of feedback that made a loud, eerie hum which could be heard everywhere at KSC that had a public address speaker. It was as if the ground receiving antennae were waiting to receive a radio transmission from the Astronauts that they were flying inbound for the Shuttle Landing Facility (SLF) at KSC for a safe landing. That was not the case. There was never a call from *Challenger* declaring an emergency with intentions to land. My colleagues at KSC who were working at the SLF with the Orbiter air conditioning and avionics cooling equipment had initiated the Orbiter recovery procedure as if the *Challenger* were approaching the runway. Everything from this point seemed futile. The Crash and Rescue Procedure could not even be worked because of the *Challenger* debris that hailed down into the Atlantic Ocean for fifty-five minutes. The NASA rescue helicopters and U.S. Air Force CH-53 Jolly Green Giant helicopters could not even enter the debris impact zone because of the hazards associated with being hit by Space Shuttle debris. This limitation of the rescue of the Astronauts was damning and totally frustrating.

All of the spectators seemed to be frozen in time

and place. As this event carried on, I could not think about anything before or after the event. I was transfixed on what was happening. It was not in slow motion as some people experience in accidents. Rather, it seemed to have no beginning, no end. The vehicle breakup event felt continuous and determined to happen. The breakup sequence seemed to have a mind of its own with endless duration.

There was an obvious deafening quiet that had come over the Kennedy Space Center. It was dramatic void that severely negated the thunderous noise of the Space Shuttle's engines from the liftoff. One by one, spectators who were on top of the boxcar office began to climb down to the ground. Almost no one spoke to each other. Everyone was stunned or shocked. Our minds were adjusting to the horror. The significance of this crash was obvious to everyone who witnessed it. I felt a great sense and need to gather with my colleagues for comfort as well as understanding of the catastrophe. I had a feeling or hope that perhaps the rest of the world did not see this Tragedy unfold. I felt as if only the people at KSC knew of the disaster. I did not want the death of my colleagues and the breakup of the *Challenger* to be seen by anyone who was not part of the family of space workers. The disappointment and loss was too personal and deep to go public with at that moment.

I walked from the boxcar office toward the LCC. I wanted to find out what was happening with this chaotic and helpless situation. I realized that we had also lost the Space Shuttle vehicle that would have carried the *Galileo* deep-space interplanetary probe to planet Jupiter in May, 1986. My Orbiter structures engineering team had just completed a very expensive one and one-half year Orbiter structures and cryogenic propulsion systems modification program in support of the *Galileo* mission. Those modifications were done so the Orbiter could accommodate both the nuclear powered *Galileo* space probe and the probe's hydrogen/oxygen booster called the *Centaur G-Prime*. The *Boeing Interim Upper Stage (IUS)* booster ultimately replaced the *Centaur G-Prime* booster.

On my way to the LCC, I passed a NASA engineer who had been hired only a few months ago. I asked him if he would like to go with me to the LCC to find out what happened to the *Challenger* and the Astronauts. We entered a room on the ground floor of the LCC that had computers and television scanners displayed onto several television monitors. We sat at a table in the center of the 20 ft. x 40 ft. room. The room was full of people doing the same.

NASA Select television network had fed to the commercial networks some very valuable and revealing high-altitude video. *CBS News with Dan Rather* was re-broadcasting a close-up view of the Space Shuttle in flight. It revealed a very bright, ominous, and abnormal glow from the right booster, which could be seen through the gap between the Shuttle's External Fuel Tank and the Orbiter. The video revealed the glow at about 65 seconds into flight. The vehicle broke apart at 71 to 73 seconds into flight. Dan Rather and his staff did a superb job of becoming familiar with what they were seeing from the video. The events, as reported by Rather, were neither overstated nor under-stated.

I saw something technically revealing about the Space Shuttle breakup sequence as I watched the tele-vision video replays. I ran to my Branch Manager's office to tell my fellow engineers and bosses what I had seen. It seemed to me that a phenomenon was apparent on the video of the Space Shuttle breakup that was significant, and could possibly be what caused such a catastrophic failure of the Space Shuttle.

After arriving at my office at Complex-A where the Space Shuttle Vehicle Engineering Directorate was located, I told my Branch Manager for Structures and Mechanisms, Mr. Ken Colley, what I had just seen on television. He was momentarily still and speechless. He regained his composure and said, "Call the Mechanical Division into my office and brief the engineers."

Ken's office was about 15 ft. x 25 ft. in area. We stuffed about 35 engineers into that little office. I used the new white marker board to describe what I'd seen on the *CBS* replay.

CHAPTER 6

DISBELIEF

We engineers were standing shoulder-to-shoulder in the Branch Manager's office. Included in this gathering were engineers from Structures, Mechanisms, Thermal Protection, External Fuel Tank, Solid Rocket Boosters, Pyrotechnics, Optical Alignment, Payload Handling, Particle Contamination, Purge Vent & Drain, and the managers of both branches. The atmosphere in the room was one of human shock and grief.

I briefed my colleagues that *CBS News* had replayed a video feed from the *NASA Select* network that clearly showed a bright concentrated glow emanating from the right hand SRB. I referred to the high-altitude camera angle that viewed the Space Shuttle close-up with a view through the gap between the Orbiter and the External Tank. The sky background was black and provided a useful contrast for clearly seeing the source of glowing flame that appeared to penetrate the right-hand SRB.

The source of the failure was inconclusive from the video, which showed a few seconds of vehicle flight with the bright glow present until, instantly, the vehicle catastrophically broke apart. I do not remember a time in my life when a room so crammed with people was so stunningly quiet. I could not even hear any of my colleagues breathe. Everyone in the room was in disbelief of what we thought we had just seen. I said to the engineers, "There was definitely something very wrong with that right hand SRB." Mr. Jerry De La Rosa, the Branch Manager for the branch responsible for the handling, stacking, and checkout of the SRBs, was frozen in position like a statue. Jerry was biting down firmly onto his smoking pipe as he held the pipe at his mouth with his right fist. He stared through his black framed eyeglasses at the sketch of the SRB and Orbiter on the marker board. He appeared to realize what had gone wrong with the SRB, but said nothing to confirm his thoughts. Jerry knew that he and his branch were in serious long-term trouble and would have to answer many difficult questions about the SRB handling, assembly, test and checkout procedures. The KSC issues would not be so much about the SRB design, but about the handling, stacking, maintenance, recovery, and inspection of the SRBs. NASA's Marshall Space Flight Center (MSFC) in Huntsville, Alabama would have to answer questions regarding the design, test firing qualification, and NASA's customer acceptance of the SRB issues.

Our Space Shuttle Program Branch and Division Managers of the 1980s had been young, new NASA engineers when the *Apollo* 1 spacecraft fire occurred at Cape Canaveral on the launch Pad in 1966. The *Apollo* 13 spacecraft had traveled halfway to the Moon in 1970 when the *Apollo* spacecraft had a failure and explosion of the cryogenic oxygen life support system. Our Space Shuttle Program managers of 1986 had been NASA engineers during the *Apollo* 13 failure. On January 28, 1986, many of those same men and women were facing the toughest duty of their careers. The difference of responsibility between 1966 and 1986 was that they had much more responsibility as NASA managers for the success or failure of the Space Shuttle than they did as engineers in *Apollo*. Everyone realized that the jobs that pay the big bucks come with answering big questions when reality deals a situation such as the *Challenger* Tragedy.

A few other engineers joined us in that small office–Ivan Velez, John Fraley, Frank Jones, Henry Crunk, Larry Rayburn, and Paul Schmitt began to ask some specific questions regarding the *CBS News* broadcast. Everyone was devastated that the flight and mission had been lost. Our friends were dead and our work was only beginning. We were still physically and emotionally exhausted from the seven *Columbia* countdowns. Now this.

In that office briefing, we concluded that there would certainly be more data, video, and evidence that would help us to understand the events of the day. We told all of our engineers to keep in touch and to be prepared for anything. We also informed everyone that all data, drawings, documents, files, and general government property was to be impounded and left in the same condition as when the launch occurred. Everyone was dismissed from the briefing and the engineers went to their desk areas to be alone or to console other colleagues and friends.

I stayed in my branch manager's office with Ken Colley, the Branch Manager, and my engineering colleague, John Fraley. We turned on the television to get the latest video and information regarding the launch. *NASA Select* television and *CBS News* were showing the same video that I had just briefed. Ken and John agreed that what I had reported seemed to be valid. Jerry De La Rosa came back into the office to see what we were seeing. Jerry was still in silent shock, while still biting his smoking pipe. I felt pity for his condition, but about the SRBs I felt that he knew something that he wasn't telling. Jerry was a NASA manager who kept matters of his engineers quiet. That type of management style alienated other engineering groups and is partially the reason that other NASA engineers knew little about the detailed components of the SRB design.

The television broadcast from *NASA Select* contained many critically important clues about the breakup sequence of *Challenger*. What looked like a chaotic conflagration of rocket propellants and hardware fragments in the sky was actually a complex record of scientific evidence that would help to prove what had caused the crash. It just looked like total destruction of the vehicle, the Astronauts, and the payload. Then, just like a flying bullet, the entire forward fuselage section that contained the Crew Module of the Orbiter shot out of the debris field of the destroyed *Challenger*. The Crew Module section was apparently intact with windows, the Forward Reaction Control System (FRCS) module, the nose section and wheel well, and the Nose Cap that housed the Microwave Landing System (MLS) antenna, all still in one 27,000 pound piece.

The Crew Module had escaped the main chaotic debris field of *Challenger*. We could not believe what we were seeing. Everything that we would see for the next six months would be unbelievable.

We theorized that the forward fuselage, which included the Crew Module with the Astronauts inside, broke clean from the mid-body fuselage and continued upward in compliance with the laws of physics regarding ballistic trajectories. The rest of the Space Shuttle was broken into small and large pieces that developed high aerodynamic drag, a condition that rapidly decelerated the loose pieces. The relative motion between the bullet-shaped Crew Module and the debris field in the sky made the Crew Module appear to eject from the debris at a high speed. As it was later determined during the investigation, that was exactly what had occurred.

One part of the *CBS News* video replay led us to inaccurate observations, and became one of the greatest lessons of observation and deduction I have ever learned in my life. The video showed the Crew Module being ejected from the debris field like a bullet. The Crew Module pitched nose down at about twenty degrees per second, a relatively slow rate as compared to the tremendous forward velocity of 1,500-1,700 miles per hour. As the severed forward fuselage, with the Astronauts still in the Crew Module, pitched down to about a 45-60 degree angle, the entire nose sheared off from the Crew Module just in front of the Crew Module forward windows. The FRCS module and the Nose Cap were no longer part of the Crew Module.

Simultaneously, there was an extremely bright flash that radiated from the nose section as the FRCS and Nose Cap sheared away from the Crew Module. Visibility of the Crew Module was completely obscured by the radiant flash, which appeared to be so ferocious and explosive that I was certain that the Astronauts, our friends, were killed at that point in the flight. I said to Ken Colley and John Fraley, "I guess that's it. Nobody could survive that." John and Ken agreed and were experiencing as much disbelief as I was. This extraordinarily important perception of events became the focus of the public's sympathy and the evidence of litigation regarding the time and "cause of death" of the Astronauts.

But we engineers had inaccurately concluded that the Astronauts had died at that point. As the investigation revealed later, that premature conclusion about the fate of the Astronauts was far from the truth. Our selective and prejudiced minds had tricked us by looking at the video of the Orbiter's breakup sequence.

This human tendency is an important lesson of premature judgement.

John and I left Ken's office and walked through the office to our desks. Looking at other engineers in my office, it seemed everyone's mind and heart was an eternity away. We all had begun to feel the pain of the loss of the crew and the Orbiter.

Henry Crunk was a great friend of mine. Henry had worked with rocket launch Pads and handling equipment since the 1950s when he began work with the National Advisory Council on Aeronautics (NACA), the predecessor to NASA. I never had seen Henry sad or depressed until that day. After reviewing the video replay of the crash, I walked to my desk. I noticed Henry standing at one of the office windows. He was obviously despondent and was staring out the window. He was staring at the Complex 39 launch Pads A and B where so many famous launches had taken place. Perhaps the launch to be most remembered from those Pads had occurred that day from Pad B. Staring, thinking, and praying seemed to be the natural response to the overwhelming situation. I looked around in our office and many people were staring out the windows and taking private time. I tried calling my mother at my home to make sure that she was all right, but all telephone circuits were busy.

A few hours later, we all had reached a saturation point, and we left for home. That was a quiet, prayerful drive home. The previous 24 NASA Space Shuttle launches had been celebrated by the local people, visitors, and space center workers at launch parties in Cocoa Beach, Titusville, Melbourne, and Orlando. Beach sand, the ocean's surf and breeze, good music, cold beer, seafood, other party foods, and the feelings of accomplished teamwork established the ambiance of the launch parties.   For the 25th Space Shuttle launch, the Tragedy of this failed launch robbed the space workers of any reason to celebrate.   There were no launch parties, no laughing, and no reason to want to do anything but go home to our families and friends to console each other and cope with the next day together.   For the next several months, the Space Coast Area of Florida became a ghost town each day after sunset.   People were emotionally frightened and everyone was glued to *NASA Select* television and *Cable News Network (CNN)* telecasts.   Every form of news media was consumed by the developing story of the *Challenger* "Accident" and the political/economic impact of the Tragedy.

In the midst of all this grief and despair, the most trying engineering work I would ever do was to begin the next day on January 29, 1986.   I slept like a baby that night.   I awoke the morning of the 29th and realized that it wasn't a dream that the *Challenger* and her crew were gone.   I got up, had breakfast with my mother, and then drove to work with incredible anticipation for what that day would become in my life and for my colleagues.

CHAPTER 7

MY ASSIGNMENT
TO THE
Challenger INVESTIGATION

On January 29, the day after the Tragedy, I drove through the historic Cape Canaveral Air Force Station at Gate 1 along the Old Cape Road. It was a beautiful and peaceful drive past the historic launch Pads and facilities where so many people supporting the various American space programs had given so many daring sacrifices. Those space programs were *Mercury*, *Gemini*, and *Apollo*, as well as many other unmanned rocket development projects. As I drove past those facilities, I further realized the scope of the risks in the manned space flight business. Before the loss of *Challenger*, I never had such an accurate point of reference.

As I drove along, I imagined hearing the fading sounds of passionate debates, engineering arguments, training sessions, and meetings that had taken place years ago in all of those old tan-colored concrete block and steel hangar buildings. The personalities of the "Original Seven" *Mercury* Astronauts, and the memories of the *Apollo* 1 Astronauts—Gus Grissom, Roger Chaffe, and Ed White—came to mind. They were the three *Apollo* Astronauts who were killed as a result of a fire in the *Apollo* spacecraft during the *Apollo* 1 launch countdown rehearsal.

Those early space program workers conducted one dangerous launch after another, and persevered no matter what or who tried to defeat them. I needed to remember the determination of those early NASA launch teams because for the next two years, NASA and the manned space programs would come under intense scrutiny, some of it warranted, and some totally unwarranted.

I proceeded west onto the NASA Causeway from the Cape Industrial Complex and drove across the Banana River. I could see Complex 39 Pad B that was under investigation. The launch Pad was impounded and had the sad, suspicious appearance of being accused of possibly causing the Space Shuttle Tragedy. It was possible that flying debris from the Pad could have initiated damage to the Space Shuttle that may have resulted in the vehicle breakup. Pad B was a launch Pad in trouble. It was a starting place to the heavens where NASA's nightmare of January 28, 1986 had begun. I completed the drive to my office and parked.

I walked into my office in Complex-A located at Complex 39 across from the LCC and the VAB. There was an atmosphere of anticipation. I could feel and breathe nervous tension in the office unlike any time since I had been working for NASA. Everyone had digested more information about what had happened with the *Challenger* and the Astronauts. Although still in shock and grieving, I could tell that my colleagues and I were making the necessary efforts to recover our crushed spirits so that we could function.

It was obvious, yet strange, that we had much work to do. It seemed strange because all of us space workers were programmed for successful tests, checkout, launch, and landings of Space Shuttles. None of us ever wanted to be programmed for disaster and death.

NASA always provided outstanding care for its

customers' payloads, and all NASA employees were accountable for the loss of these payloads. We had participated in many meetings for emergencies, crash and rescue, and what to do if things go really wrong. One reason that we had difficulty with accepting the Tragedy was the manner in which the *Challenger* broke apart. The hail of debris, no escape system aboard the Shuttle for the Astronauts, and the anxiety of having to just stand by and watch our heroes die made the acceptance of this Tragedy most difficult.

I was called into the same office that we used to review the *Challenger* breakup video on the day of the disaster. The Branch Chief, Mr. Ken Colley, had summoned John Fraley and me and told us that a team had been established to initiate the accident investigation of the *Challenger*. John was to be on the team that scoured the launch Pad B area and the beach to look for any debris that may have fallen from the Shuttle or the Pad facilities. This effort was important to determine if any debris from the new Pad B had contributed to the vehicle breakup. Another reason to inspect the Pad and general area was to search for any signs of sabotage.

Ken said to me, "Randy, you are assigned to the Vehicle Breakup Analysis and Reconstruction Team. You are to report to the new Logistics Facility at noon today. The reason you two have been selected is because you know the Orbiter vehicle as well as anyone."

There was also another reason that John and I qualified to serve on the investigation team. In order to ensure a truthful investigation, anyone who was directly involved with the "Decision-to-Launch" could not work directly with the investigation. Later, it became clear to me that the NASA Office of General

Council (NASA attorneys) and the NTSB made sure that people with a "cover-up motive" could not have access to the evidence to manipulate the evidence. NASA was in search of the truth about the causes of this tragic crash. With the tough months that had preceded the *Challenger* disaster, NASA needed a good dose of the truth. This is one of the fundamental reasons that I have written this book. I want to show you that the *Challenger Investigation* was conducted in search for the truth. I helped investigate the *Challenger* Tragedy with some of the finest people you would ever want to know.

The investigation achieved verification of the real and whole truth. We wanted to know what had happened to *Challenger*, the Astronauts, and the payloads, and we wanted to make sure that no piece of information was ignored or overlooked. We were looking for the cause of this disaster as well as anything that would pose a threat to future Space Shuttle flights. Tragic events produce leaders of unusual capacities and capabilities. In 1986, the *Challenger* Tragedy summoned us to stretch beyond our normal responsibilities. We investigators became more skillful leaders and learned why it is necessary to include skilled people and resources to solve complex engineering problems.

What of future Space Shuttle flights? It suddenly occurred to me that this investigation could possibly be the last major job of NASA in the Manned Space Program. This assignment would be the toughest, most responsible, and most tiring work that I would ever do.

Every hour of the 28th and 29th of January was full of discussions, assignments, and events that seemed logical and understandable at first. I quickly learned that the execution of my assignments would be difficult to start because my mind was not set to think along the lines of disaster, death, and a destroyed Space Shuttle vehicle and payload. This was a very depressing element of the initial days of the investigation.

For example, I was assigned to work at the new Logistics Facility with the Vehicle Breakup Analysis. I had never been in the new NASA Logistics Facility. It is a multi-million dollar facility for warehousing Shuttle Program parts. I walked over to the facility at 11:30 A.M. on January 29, just 24 hours after the Tragedy, and arrived on the rear loading dock where several other NASA, Lockheed, and Rockwell employees were gathering for the same reason.

I felt like I was at the wrong place. In an emotional way, I felt like I needed to be in meetings, or doing an analysis—or something, anything—to solve the puzzle of why did this disaster occur? Instead, there I was on the loading dock of the Logistics Facility.

Ron Phelps was in charge of the investigation operation at the Logistics Facility. He was a NASA Test Director (NTD). Ron's normal work environment was in the Firing Rooms. My normal work environment was inside a Space Shuttle Orbiter, stacking the Space Shuttle upon the MLP inside the VAB, launch preparations on the Pad, or recovery of an Orbiter at the landing sites. We were all going through adjustments by the hour. Events of those days were totally unpredictable. We reacted by making decisions as the most unusual problems and events occurred. We had to work that way because there was no other choice. Our lives had become slaves to determining the causes of the Tragedy.

Jobs and services like we were having to perform during the investigation made me appreciate the days that I paid attention in school, asked questions, learned about why my view of the world is not the only view of the world. I was so thankful that I had additional education in college to prepare me for what I was now going through. I had learned the nuts and bolts of the Space Shuttle Program—everything that I could. I had worked for NASA eight years and five months at the time of the disaster. My mind was focused upon the deceased Astronauts, the American public, and the NASA management. I was committed to doing an honest investigation.

I still had not figured out why I was assigned to the Logistics Facility, which seemed so far removed from the action of investigating the crash. What in the heavens were we to do at a logistics facility? In seven days I would find the answer to that question.

President Reagan issued an **Executive Order, E. O.** *12546*, on February 3, 1986, that established the *Rogers Presidential Commission on the <u>Challenger</u> Accident*, and the Commission members were sworn in to duty on February 6, 1986.

PRESIDENTIAL COMMISSION MEMBERS ON THE SPACE SHUTTLE *CHALLENGER* ACCIDENT

ROGERS PRESIDENTIAL COMMISSION MEMBERS:

WILLIAM P. ROGERS, CHAIRMAN
Former Secretary of State under President Nixon (1969-1973), and Attorney General under President Eisenhower (1957-1961), currently a practicing attorney and senior partner in the law firm of Rogers & Wells. Born in Norfolk, New York, he was awarded the Medal of Freedom in 1973.

He holds a J.D. from Cornell University (1937) and served as LCDR, U.S. Navy (1942-1946).

Neil A. Armstrong, Vice Chairman

Former astronaut, currently Chairman of the Board of Computing Technologies for Aviation, Inc. Born in Wapakoneta, Ohio, Mr. Armstrong was spacecraft commander for *Apollo* 11, July 16-24, 1969, the first Manned Lunar landing mission. He was Professor of Aeronautical Engineering at the University of Cincinnati from 1971 to 1980 and was appointed to the National Commission on Space in 1985.

David C. Acheson

Former Senior Vice President and General Counsel, Communications Satellite Corporation (1967-1974), currently a partner in the law firm of Drinker, Biddle & Reath. Born in Washington, DC, he previously served as an attorney with the U.S. Atomic Energy Commission (1948-1950) and was U.S. Attorney for the District of Columbia (1961-1965). He holds an LL.B. from Harvard University (1948) and served as LT, U.S. Navy (1942-1946).

Dr. Eugene E. Covert

Educator and engineer. Born in Rapid City, South Dakota, he is currently Professor and Head, Department of

Aeronautics and Astronautics, at Massachusetts Institute of Technology. Member of the National Academy of Engineering, he was a recipient of the Exceptional Civilian Service Award, U.S. Air Force, in 1973 and the NASA Public Service Award in 1980. He holds a Doctorate in Science from Massachusetts Institute of Technology.

DR. RICHARD P. FEYNMAN
Physicist. Born in New York City, he is Professor of Theoretical Physics at California Institute of Technology. Nobel Prize winner in Physics, 1965, he also received the Einstein Award in 1954, the Oersted Medal in 1972 and the Niels Bohr International Gold Medal in 1973. He holds a Doctorate in Physics from Princeton (1942).

ROBERT B. HOTZ
Editor, publisher. Born in Milwaukee, Wisconsin. He is a graduate of Northwestern University. He was the editor-in-chief of Aviation Week & Space Technology Magazine (1953-1980). He served in the U.S. Air Force in World War II and was awarded the Air Medal with Oak Leaf Cluster. Since 1982, he has been a member of the General Advisory Committee to the Arms Control and Disarmament Agency.

Major General Donald J. Kutyna

U.S. Air Force Director of Space Systems and Command, Control, Communications. Born in Chicago, Illinois, and graduate of the U.S. Military Academy, he holds a Master of Science degree from Massachusetts Institute of Technology (1965). A Command Pilot with over 4,000 flight hours, he is a recipient of the Distinguished Service Medal, Distinguished Flying Cross, Legion of Merit and nine air medals.

Dr. Sally K. Ride

Astronaut. Born in Los Angeles, California, she was a Mission Specialist on STS-7, launched on June 18, 1983, becoming the first American woman in space. She also flew on Mission 41-G launched October 5, 1984. She holds a Doctorate in Physics from Stanford University (1978) and is still an active Astronaut.

Robert W. Rummel

Space expert and aerospace engineer. Born in Dakota, Illinois, and former Vice President of Trans World Airlines, he is currently President of Robert W. Rummel Associates, Inc., of Mesa, Arizona. He is a member of the National Academy of Engineering and is holder of the NASA Distinguished Public Service Medal.

JOSEPH F. SUTTER

Aeronautical Engineer. Currently Executive Vice President of the Boeing Commercial Airplane Company. Born in Seattle, he has been with Boeing since 1945 and was a principal figure in the development of three generations of jet aircraft. In 1984, he was elected to the National Academy of Engineering. In 1985, President Reagan conferred on him the U.S. National Medal of Technology.

DR. ARTHUR B. C. WALKER, JR.

Astronomer. Born in Cleveland, Ohio, he is currently Professor of Applied Physics and was formerly Associate Dean of the Graduate Division at Stanford University. Consultant to Aerospace Corporation, Rand Corporation and the National Science Foundation, he is a member of the American Physical Society, American Geophysical Union, and the American Astronomy Society. He holds a Doctorate in Physics from the University of Illinois (1962).

DR. ALBERT D. WHEELON

Physicist. Born in Moline, Illinois, he is currently Executive Vice President, Hughes Aircraft Company. Also a member of the President's Foreign Intelligence Advisory Board, he served as a consultant to the President's Science Advisory Council from 1961 to 1974. He holds a Doctorate in Physics from Massachusetts Institute of Technology (1952).

BRIGADIER GENERAL CHARLES YEAGER
U.S. Air Force (Retired) Former Experimental Test Pilot. Born in Myra, West Virginia, he was appointed in 1985 as a member of the National Commission on Space. He was the first person to penetrate the sound barrier and the first to fly at a speed of more than 1,600 miles an hour.

DR. ALTON G. KEEL, JR.
Executive Director Detailed to the Commission from his position in the Executive Office of the President, Office of Management and Budget, as Associate Director for National Security and International Affairs; formerly Assistant Secretary of the U.S. Air Force for Research, Development and Logistics; and Senate Staff. Born in Newport News, Virginia, he holds a Doctorate in Engineering Physics from the University of Virginia (1970).

(Source: The Presidential Commission on the Space Shuttle *Challenger* Accident Report, June 6, 1986)

Presidential Mandate of the Commission:

1. Review the circumstances surrounding the accident to establish the probable causes of the accident.
2. Develop recommendations for corrective or other actions based upon the Commission's findings and determinations.

The Presidential Report contains a Preface on page P1 that reads as follows:

Preface

"For the first several days after the accident—possibly because of the trauma resulting from the accident—NASA appeared to be withholding information about the accident from the public. After the Commission began its work and at its suggestion, NASA began releasing a great deal of information that helped to reassure the public that all aspects of the accident were being investigated and that the full story was being told in an orderly and thorough manner.

Following the suggestion of the Commission, NASA established several teams of persons not involved in the Mission 51-L launch process to support the Commission and its panels. These NASA teams have cooperated with the Commission in every aspect of its work. The result has been a comprehensive and complete investigation.

The Commission believes that its investigation and report have been responsive to the request of the President and hopes that they will serve the best interests of the nation in restoring the United States Space Program to its preeminent position in the world."

The Presidential Report on The Challenger Accident was presented to President Ronald Reagan on June 6, 1986, only four months and nine days after the tragic conclusion of the *Challenger* 51-L mission.

The decision had been made to designate the Logistics Facility as the primary facility to stage the wreckage of the Orbiter *Challenger* for breakup analysis, documentation, and disposition for burial. I realized that I had been assigned to the most critical and sensitive part of the investigation. This experience was the "big leagues." I had to be about my work.

Ron Phelps conducted the first meeting of the Breakup Analysis/Reconstruction Team in the large high-bay area of the Logistics Facility. We discussed why we were there, where to get equipment that we needed, what the rules were, and that all shifts would be at least twelve hours, back-to-back, round the clock. We were reminded that all of us had Secret level NASA clearances with U.S. Air Force area clearance codes called PACAS (pronounced *Pack-us*). All appropriate security rules and practices would be in effect for this assignment. We were given the opportunity to refuse the assignment if we so chose. I doubt that anybody even thought of quitting.

Then, the strangest of events occurred. Ron told us that a floor grid needed to be made to provide a reference grid to locate the Orbiter pieces in an as-built fashion. I recall thinking, "What Orbiter pieces might he be talking about"? The pieces that we saw in the sky the day before were at the bottom of the Atlantic Ocean or floating with the currents. We did not realize the scope of salvage and recovery operations that were forming in concert with our activities involving NASA SRB retrieval ships, the U.S. Coast Guard, the U.S. Navy, the U.S. Air Force, and other elements such as Navy Seals, and robotic submersibles. That nautical operation was getting larger by the hour. We had to remain in communication with certain people to become aware of teams that were forming all over the

Kennedy Space Center, other NASA centers, government agencies, and local law enforcement offices.

None of us on this team had been inside the new Logistics Facility prior to the crash. We could not imagine putting an entire Shuttle Orbiter inside this site. That is one reason that it seemed odd that the Breakup Analysis/Reconstruction Team duty station was at this facility. Where would we put an Orbiter? Where would we put the ET, SRBs and the payload? Most of all, how much of the Space Shuttle would we even have to work with at all? After seeing the in-flight breakup, it was difficult to believe that anything was recoverable.

I started working immediately. I asked a Lockheed quality inspector, Mr. Kelly Longhofer, to help me put three-inch wide bright yellow tape onto the concrete floor in the high-bay area to form the reference grid. After a couple of hours we had completed the grid. At this point, our conceptions of Space Shuttle parts were thoughts of nice, healthy, flight-worthy parts. We had not yet imagined the reality of parts that had been destroyed.

The team established an office area at the southeast corner of the building. We later enclosed the office with heavy gauge wire fencing with a steel frame. This type of fencing is commonly seen installed in front of windows to deter break-ins. We selected various documents, drawings, photos, and equipment that we felt would be necessary to help us identify, log, document, and photograph the Shuttle wreckage.

I went to the Technical Data Center, an office with a counter where we regularly ordered drawings and other documents. There was a teen-aged young man working behind the counter. I filled out the pink order card to acquire an Orbiter drawing set and gave the card to him. He went to retrieve the drawing and came back in about two minutes. He said, "I cannot give you that drawing because it's a master drawing. We only have three copies. I can send the drawing out to reproduction and it will be back in about two weeks." I said to him, "I don't think you realize what is happening with the investigation. I work for NASA and here is my secret clearance. Since you are one of our government contractors, I am authorizing you to give me that drawing. There is a chance that you will be laid off in a few days because of the *Challenger* Tragedy. Just give me the drawings and I will explain this to your supervisor." He gave me the master drawing and I took it to the Logistics Facility. I wasn't trying to be unreasonable, but I was tired and we had to have the drawing set. We used that drawing many times, but our basic recall was the most valuable source of information.

That day was very long and unpredictable, a sign of the days to come. I went home, ate supper, bathed, and watched television channels *Cable News Network* and *ABC* Channel 9 of Orlando, Florida to hear what the news media was reporting about the *Challenger* crash investigation operations. I went to bed exhausted and slept for about twelve hours.

CHAPTER 8

THE FIRST FLATBED TRUCK
OF
Challenger DEBRIS

Several days had passed since the *Challenger* crash. The national and local news companies had saturated news broadcasts with *"Challenger* Accident" news. Competition between various news-reporting companies has always been an element of the space business. Most of the news about the *Challenger* crash that was finally read, heard, and watched was appropriate and professional. The Press appeared to produce compassionate, sincere, and thoughtful reporting. The information gathering was done quickly and the reporting was generally clear and to the point. Reporters and editors from around the world rapidly became "experts" on Space Shuttle systems.

Those reporters in the news media who have scooped major stories, have camped out in the freezing rain, have prayed for mosquitoes to die, or goodness knows what else, know that competition was fierce for the story about the *Challenger* crash. Any reporter who filed the "confirmed" story first, and made it to print or broadcast, became the winning reporter. The only regulating factor about the "Reporter Races" to the printer and broadcasters was that all news media were saturated with reports and information about the *Challenger* crash. There was too much information for anyone to assimilate.

There were the typical newsmen and news-women who, during the investigation, tried to "go beyond the ropes" and were tossed out of restricted areas. During the investigation, someone had placed phone taps on NASA phone lines. Most restaurants in the area had dozens of curious reporters who were "new to the area" and just wanted to ask, "What do you do for a living?" "What do you think about that terrible Shuttle accident?"

I had heard NASA briefings and news reports that the salvage operations in the Atlantic Ocean were making great progress in finding and recovering *Challenger* debris. NASA had already produced a trajectory and water impact analysis that pinpointed the various Space Shuttle debris impact zones in the Atlantic Ocean. The media reports were implying that NASA was having difficulties locating the debris critical to determining the cause of the accident. None of those reports were true, and NASA was not covering up the developments of the salvage operation.

One day in February 1986, I was in Cocoa Beach visiting my friends when a television broadcast interrupted the regular broadcast to "bring you this breaking story about the *Challenger* retrieval operations." The commentator said, "NASA has located the Crew Module of the *Challenger* on the floor of the Atlantic Ocean." That report was perhaps the first misleading report of many that were published by some of the news organizations. It implied that NASA did not previously know the location in the ocean of the Crew Module that contained the Astronaut corpses. NASA knew exactly where the Crew Module debris was located on the ocean floor. NASA realized that the location of the Crew Module was a hot story. The sensationalism of that report misled the public and disappointed us at NASA.

I was working the noon-to-midnight shift on the

Sunday after the Tragedy occurred. I will never forget that day. The Breakup Analysis/Reconstruction Team was briefed at the beginning of the shift that the first flatbed truck of Space Shuttle wreckage that had been salvaged from the ocean would be arriving near sundown.

I had a nervous feeling of "butterflies" in my stomach just thinking about seeing the *Challenger* wreckage. Something upsetting was surely about to happen. The investigation team had been so busy preparing for the debris to arrive that a psychological denial of the crash had developed in our minds. Who wouldn't be in denial? The horror of the crash was too much for our minds, and our hearts were broken for many reasons. At that point, I had not envisioned what a flatbed of *Challenger* debris would be like.

That afternoon, the Sun was a bright golden color and was close to setting when we got the call from the U.S. Navy docks at Port Canaveral. That golden sunset and the ringing of the telephone will always be vivid in my memory. I often think of that moment when I see a magnificent sunset. The phone calls to our location were updates from our investigators who were located at the Cape Canaveral U.S. Navy Port. The calls were updated regarding the progress of the truck hauling the *Challenger*'s wreckage to us at the Logistics Facility. We were about to see *Challenger* again, but in a form greatly altered from what was *Challenger*, that reliable spaceship that we had built. The telephone calls informed us that the first flatbed of *Challenger* debris was rolling to KSC in route to the Logistics Facility via the Old Cape Road, NASA Causeway, Merritt Parkway, Contractor Road, into the side parking lot of the Logistics Facility, with a final turn into the rear loading dock area.

When Ron Phelps got off the first phone call he said, "Okay, get ready guys, the truck is rolling." Every one of us on that loading dock was silent. No one seemed comfortable looking each other in the eyes. Each person seemed to look down at the concrete loading dock in deep thought and slowly and nervously walked around. I walked to the south end of the loading dock to view that magnificent sunset.

It seemed as though it took an hour for the flatbed truck to travel the twenty miles or so. I felt as if we were alone and no one could possibly understand the collision of emotions that all of the team was feeling. There was a mix of camaraderie and anxiety over having to watch something that we did not want to see. Yet my curiosity was mounting. I began to wonder what a flatbed of Shuttle debris would look like. I wasn't comfortable with those images and immediately put them out of my mind. I chatted about insignificant things with my team members to focus away from our nervousness. The team had to be 100% ready to go so that we would not disappoint anyone in our performance.

Ron Phelps continued to get location updates of the flatbed. We were aware of the truck's position for the entire route. Finally, we could hear and see coming down the road the NASA Security escort leading the way for the truck. The lead security cars with blue lights flashing turned aside as they entered the parking lot of the Logistics Facility to make way for the flatbed truck to continue to the rear of the facility. The white NASA eighteen-wheeler truck aggressively drove into the asphalt loading dock area. The truck driver stopped, shifted the truck gears into reverse, and slowly backed up to the loading dock under the direction of two of the technicians and Ron Phelps. I still have memories of the trailer's red lights and the sound of the airbrakes venting pressure as the truck backed toward the dock.   On the flatbed trailer were olive-colored canvas tarps secured over the lumpy contents beneath.

I was just staring at the olive tarps that were full of whatever was under them.   There appeared to be a lot of stuff under those tarps.   Somehow, that was surprising.   My mind had not determined what size of debris I might see.   With the tarps in place I was not sure if there were lots of small pieces or just a few large pieces.   I would soon find out.

The truck driver completed backing up to the dock bumpers, switched the engine off, and set the brakes.   We all just stared at the tarps for what seemed like a long time but was actually only a couple of minutes.   Ron said, "Well, let's get to work."

I stepped onto the flatbed from the dock and we began to untie the tarps.   As we removed the rear half, I was surprised and dismayed by what I saw.   I immediately recognized one of the Ammonia Boilers that had been part of the *Challenger* in the upper section of the engine compartment.   The Ammonia Boilers boil pure ammonia to provide heat transfer to cool the Orbiter avionics to prevent overheating of the electrical black boxes.   The Ammonia Boilers operate below 100,000 feet during reentry from orbit and continue to provide cooling through landing.   I couldn't believe that I was seeing an old acquaintance and artifact from the Orbiter's engine compartment.   I remembered when the Ammonia Boilers were installed into *Challenger* years before the disaster.

We attempted to remove the Ammonia Boilers from the flatbed truck and realized how unprepared we were for such an unusual operation as this vehicle retrieval and reconstruction. We needed a forklift. There was no way to deal with this twisted, crushed mess of *Challenger*. *Challenger?* It finally became reality to me that *this* was *Challenger*. Unimaginable. I had a sinking feeling that this was the tip of the iceberg. I could only imagine what the rest of the Space Shuttle wreckage looked like.

We were somewhat uncoordinated or awkward in removing the *Challenger* pieces from the truck to the loading dock. There was a sense of relationship regarding the *Challenger* wreckage. It was similar to the feelings you may have had when viewing the body of a deceased person whom you have known for years. Although the body is dead or destroyed, your thoughts recall the times that were shared. The feeling was one of realizing that better times like those shared have come to an end. It took several days for that emotion to diminish. That feeling diminished because we had gotten so busy with the science and labors of the crash investigation.

We were so unprepared for such a bizarre duty that faced us at the Logistics Facility that we placed the *Challenger* pieces on the dock without moving the pieces directly into the main high-bay of the Logistics Facility. We simply did not desire to be holding the broken pieces of *Challenger*. *Challenger* was a superb flying machine with a long history of contributions and achievements to the United States Space Program. I detested seeing it in this form.

We finally moved the entire load of *Challenger* pieces from the dock into the high-bay area. We located the pieces in their proper grid location on the floor that represented the aft fuselage engine compartment. Those parts looked pitiful sitting there on the concrete floor.

I am using the word "we" more frequently at this point. The individuals who were assigned to the Breakup Analysis were becoming a united team. We united out of commitment to "do good work" as Gus Grissom, a former *Mercury* and *Gemini* Astronaut, used to say. We united from our own fears. We had no time to mourn the loss of our friends, the vehicle, or the Mission.

Mr. Kelly Longhofer, Mr. Gene Rossiter, and I started the first page of the official logbook to record the description, quantity, and pertinent information about each piece of the *Challenger* retrieved. Mr. Louie Roquevert, the NASA contracted Technicolor photographer who had worked at KSC for decades, had been assigned to take the photographs for the documentation of the *Challenger* parts. Before the *Challenger* disaster, Louie was always available in the Orbiter Processing Facility, the launch Pads, the Shuttle Landing Facility (SLF), the payload processing cleanrooms, and virtually everywhere I had worked in better times with *Challenger.* Louie had tearful, attentive eyes that day. He was always reliable and professional in photographing the exact items that engineering, quality, and operations determined necessary. The *Challenger* debris photos were no exception. Louie had a meek personality and was the best photographer in our business. He was a critical part of the NASA and contractor team, and everyone at KSC who worked with him came to love him.

The Breakup Analysis and Reconstruction Team worked about fifteen hours that day. We had performed activities that we would not have imagined just days before. The Sun had long ago set on this day. We were into the next day. From this time onward, most of us investigators could not tell which day of the week it was. It really didn't matter. We had a huge task in front of us to complete. We were responsible to discover the cause or causes of the disaster, find any other problems that could become a cause of future possible crashes, and help solve the many questions regarding the failure of the Space Shuttle vehicle. What had really gone wrong? Did anyone really know the answers? We had to discover those answers.

I drove home after midnight through the dark of the KSC National Wildlife Refuge with so much on my mind. I was mourning the deaths of the Astronauts and hoping that I would be able to cope with those feelings. But this is only the beginning of this space flight story.

CHAPTER 9

LONG DAYS AND NIGHTS WITH *Challenger*

The following days came too quickly. It began to seem as if we were in a time compression with too much work to do. The Logistics Facility was beginning to fill up with pieces of *Challenger.* The U.S. Army from White Sands, New Mexico shipped a massive air-inflated Quonset-style temporary building. It was assembled on the asphalt area behind the Logistics Facility in the southeast corner. The large pieces of the External Tank and the forward and aft sections of the Solid Rocket Boosters (known as Frustrums and Aft Skirts) were placed in that building.

The debris Impound and Analysis area at the Logistics Facility was expanded to include a fenced area located about 40 yards behind the loading dock. That area was composed of several buildings that were part of the overall Logistics Facility. This fenced area was never intended to support an accident investigation of a Space Shuttle, but contained what was called the POL (Paint/Oil Locker) area, which was a white metal carport-style structure with steel I-beam supports to support the metal roof, and a concrete floor with drain sumps in the low points of the concrete floor. This structure became very famous because that is where the *Challenger* Crew Module was placed for the Vehicle Breakup Analysis work after retrieval from the Atlantic Ocean.

During the period when the Space Shuttle wreckage was retrieved and brought ashore, almost every news reporter who covered the *Challenger* accident investigation was trying to find out where the Orbiter's Crew Module was located.   NASA wasn't telling where it was, and the reporters were not successful in determining its location.   The accident investigators, NASA security, and the alligators of the National Wildlife Refuge combined to provide solitude in the form of highly restricted and guarded areas. The restricted areas of the new Logistics Facility became the new home for the Crew Module wreckage and for the small number of us investigators who were authorized to work in that restricted area.

Olive-colored   military   tarps   were   hung vertically between the I-beam supports of the carport structure to provide cover so that no one could see the Crew Module or investigators. We were only about half a mile from the KSC Complex 39 Press Site where small armies of reporters for news wire services, radio, television, and newspapers were competitively composing their *Challenger* stories for the public.   The wind that blew across the *Challenger* Crew Module pieces that winter and spring of 1986 also blew across the Press Site.   None of those bloodhound reporters ever had a clue that the Crew Module wreckage was so close. Had they found out where the Crew Module was, we would have expanded the restricted area. The appearance of "normal operations" was our decoy to keep the location of the Crew Module secret. The reporters for the news wire services were the most determined, and in my opinion, the most accurate reporters of the investigation.   They functioned as an effective check and   balance   for   assuring   the   public   that   the investigation progressed in an ethical manner.

Behind the carport structure, about twenty feet to the east, were about ten three-wall bays that were connected together and built of white concrete blocks.

A metal roof covered all of the bays and was similar to the carport structure roof. Most of the Crew Module electrical wiring was placed in these bays, along with various Crew Module pieces including the window frames. There was a large drainage sump in the open-air concrete driveway that was located between the carport and the bays.

Just 30 feet to the south of the carport structure, a substantial concrete block and steel building contained a refrigerated room with a large sealed door. When the door was opened, there were clear plastic vertical curtains to save the cold air inside the room. That refrigerated room was the cold storage area for the Crew Module seats, crew helmets, articles from the stowage lockers, and other various items that came in direct contact with the Astronaut remains. Those items could have had biological evidence on them that may have answered questions. The refrigerated room was very unsettling. We had to work there, and although there were no Astronaut bodies inside, most of us preferred to stand near or just outside the doorway. Our nerves were not their best at this point.

There was a small building behind and to the east of the refrigerated room that contained the payload that had been in the *Challenger* cargo bay. The very expensive contents of that room were the fractured and twisted remnants of what had been pristine payloads from the Orbiter. The hardware consisted of the NASA Tracking Data Relay Satellite (TDRS), valued at about $150 million and had been mounted atop the solid booster motor called the Interim Upper Stage (IUS). The other major payload element was the optical payload that was to film or video Haley's Comet passing "near" the Earth at its closest point in 1986. The payload was a broken, tangled mess that included the composite fibrous structures of the IUS motor nozzle. The extremely tough nozzle of the IUS was literally torn to shreds. The composite fibers were exposed and loose.

A high chain-link fence that had only a couple of gates for access surrounded the entire POL area. Only one gate was open on a continuing basis and that gate had a NASA armed security guard or two, at all times, 24 hours a day, seven days a week. Anyone who approached that security checkpoint with improper or inadequate credentials was in trouble. There were very few people who ever got clearance into that area where the Crew Module was located. If a person was not assigned to work in that area or had no need to know what was in that area, they were turned away. In some cases, unauthorized people were escorted totally away from the Logistics Facility.

The entire work experience in the Crew Module and payload debris area was a combination of very focused, physical, and critical work. The past, present, and future of the Space Shuttle Program and manned space flight was all in jeopardy and literally under the microscope at the Crew Module debris investigation area. I was aware of all of those factors from the beginning of the investigation. The pressure of responsibility would not let up for a single day until the work was complete and the *Rogers Presidential Commission Report on the Challenger Accident Investigation* was submitted to President Reagan.

It was comforting to know that we were always protected from unauthorized intruders by NASA security. At night the swamp fog settled over the National Wildlife Refuge behind the Crew Module wreckage area. The eerie calm and still of a foggy night at Complex 39, combined with the deaths of our colleagues, was a real test of our nerves. All of us were on edge. Seven deaths had taken place and they were our friends.

I spent many strenuous and stressful nights by myself amongst the *Challenger* Crew Module wreckage, with the NASA security guard about eighty feet away around the corner. NASA Security did a fabulous job of minimizing the numbers of people in the restricted area. The process makes for lonely work areas. The death, or future, of our Space Program would be determined from the secrets contained within the *Challenger* wreckage that rested all around me on the cold concrete floor. My heart was saddened each time I saw the *Challenger's* Crew Module pieces. I, like so many other people, had worked so hard for so many years to make that Crew Module close to perfect and clean. NASA workers always strived for a high level of safety while understanding the hazards and risks. *Challenger's* wreckage was confirming proof that NASA workers were not perfect and that important vehicle design flaws had been missed.

My work with the *Challenger* Crew Module had begun several years earlier in 1977 through 1981. I had worked with that Crew Module when it was in Palmdale, California at Rockwell International before it was officially named *Challenger.* The Crew Module was installed into a high fidelity Orbiter look-alike that was used to check the fit of components and systems before they were installed into Orbiter *Columbia* that was under construction. The Orbiter fit-check mockup was called *Structural Test Article 099, STA-099.* NASA's original plans for the Shuttle Program did not envision the *STA-099* as a flight qualified Orbiter. Throughout the decade of the 1970s, the U.S. Congress never adequately funded NASA with the money to build the six Orbiters planned for the Space Shuttle Program. The budgetary compromise forced NASA to upgrade *STA-099* to flight configuration and quality that would result in only four Orbiters total. *STA-099* became the second flight-qualified Orbiter built. She was named *Challenger.*

Hungry raccoons visited us most nights at the wreckage area. Their comical actions often lifted our spirits. The night shift from 8 P.M. to 8 A.M. was very slow for the first two hours, and tended to drag from 4-5 A.M., but the early morning lunch break was a treat. There were glorious sunrises each day and the Sun's rays shined onto the broken pieces of *Challenger* and dried the Atlantic Ocean barnacles that were still attached to the debris.

The flatbed trucks of *Challenger* debris continued the relentless parade at the Logistics Facility, one after another.   As the days passed, I became totally immersed in the details of the Crew Module Reconstruction and Breakup Analysis.   Most of my work during 1986 focused on the reconstruction of the Orbiter's main assemblies such as the fuselage, wings, aft fuselage or engine compartment, and many internal subsystems. The legal, political, and technical importance of the Crew Module had grown to an astounding level of concern and efforts.   The sensitivity and accuracy of our work had never been so critical. There were so many tasks that were being worked and so many complex problems to solve.

My supervisor, Ken Colley, and the debris site manager, Ron Phelps, directed me to apply my full attention and work to the component identification, reconstruction, and breakup analysis of the Crew Module debris and the Astronauts biological effects that would be found in the debris. This new focus on the Crew Module developed because of the relentless questions regarding the time and cause of death of the Astronauts. The public, reporters, family members, other Astronauts, lawyers, coroners, and NASA wanted to know exactly when and how the *Challenger* Astronauts died.

Biological evidence found in the Crew Module debris was documented and then refrigerated for transfer from KSC to Hangar L that was located across the Banana River, on the Cape Canaveral Air Force Station. Hangar L, one of the original hangars that were built for the *Mercury* Program of the early 1960s, had previously been converted for the Space Shuttle Program to process and refurbish the life support system components of the Orbiter's air recycling and refurbishment system. Hangar L had much of the necessary equipment to allow for the quick and efficient setup of the pathological investigation area having to do with the Astronaut corpses. I never entered that facility because I was not assigned to that area and had "no need to know" by design. NASA did well to partition the investigation elements so that independent accident investigation efforts and results could be checked and balanced.

The biological findings from my work area were submitted as findings or discoveries. Highly qualified doctors and scientists, such as NASA Flight Surgeon Dr. Joseph Kerwin at JSC, conducted an integrated comparison of our biological and hardware findings in the Crew Module wreckage area with the pathological findings at Hangar L. My confidence is secure regarding the final conclusions about the cause of deaths of the Astronauts contained in the *Rogers Presidential Commission Report on the Challenger Accident Investigation* because I observed and worked within the architecture of the well-partitioned and properly integrated methodologies of crash investigation. I stand by our findings.

There were many nights when I would be working with Mr. Kelly Longhofer, my Quality Control Technician. Other nights I would be working alone. I would sense the full awareness that I was standing or sitting amongst the actual Flight Deck or Mid Deck of the *Challenger*. I thought about how the seats and instruments were exposed to the final sounds and actions of the crew. It was not too difficult to imagine the crew sitting in their seats in exasperation due to the inability to change their circumstances after the breakup in flight. Many times I had to shake my head and blink my eyes in an effort to reorient my mind to be able to continue my work.

CHAPTER 10

I'VE LOST MY COLLEAGUES
AND
THE OTHER ORBITERS

Many weeks had passed since the day of the Tragedy. The investigation team members had become totally fatigued and somewhat depressed. I was longing to see my NASA and contractor engineers, technicians, and quality control colleagues with whom I normally worked. I did not know the status of my regular daily colleagues, or even what responsibilities they had been assigned. It seemed as if my colleagues were taken away, but it was we investigators who were segregated from them to ensure an honest investigation of the Tragedy.

The NASA contractors, which included Lockheed, Rockwell, and others, had laid off about 7,000 employees at KSC since the *Challenger* crash. I wasn't sure that I would ever see some of those people again. I was also feeling pity for the good managers who had done their specific jobs well, but had become caught in the web of flawed decisions to launch the 51-L Mission. If only those men and women had called for a scrub of the launch countdown. Would NASA or the contractors have punished them for such a launch scrub? Possibly, but leadership with courage and making the right decision and acting on it is always more respectable.

I had not thought of, or seen, an intact and undamaged Orbiter in weeks. That was a total change in my routine and actions of times before the breakup of *Challenger*. As the winter faded and the spring season of 1986 arrived, I began to imagine what a healthy Orbiter would look like.   It would have been depressing to experience seeing an idle Orbiter in an Orbiter Processing Facility (OPF) hi-bay. It would have been disturbing to see the remaining three Orbiters sitting on Earth in 1-gravity (1-g), when, by design, the Orbiters belonged in zero-gravity in orbit.

The Space Shuttle Breakup Analysis and Reconstruction Team began to feel that the Logistics Facility had become our permanent office. We adapted to the situation and pace of the investigation like NASA people have had to do so many times in the past. We had accepted our assignments and the magic of the NASA culture was developing once again. This team was assembled because of each member's previous commitment to exactness, knowledge of the Space Shuttle, and reputation for assuring quality control. Expert procedures, testing, observation, documentation, and imagination would serve the team well in the coming days. Without control of those parameters of investigation, the identification and proof of what exactly went wrong with the Space Shuttle *Challenger* may have never been totally accomplished.

I was busy working myself into fatigue with the crash investigation. I had never worked so hard for anyone. I was one of a focused group of investigators who knew that NASA's new mission was one of justification and survival as an agency and technological leader.

The men and women at KSC were some of the most amazing people I have ever known. They were extraordinary workers with endurance and the desire to do their best amidst the challenges of life in the mid 1980s. The lifestyle challenges included long work hours, the avalanche of technological hardware at KSC, economic inflation, space program-related travel that took them away from their families, and trying to raise their families while also finding time to rest.

Work shifts often approached 24 hours and that commitment to the work established a mutual respect amongst NASA and contractor employees. I refer to those workers as contractors only for clarity in this writing. The contracted workers, approximately 15,000 people, and the government NASA workers, about 1,800, were as one workforce. Many times, Rockwell and Lockheed engineers thought that I was a contractor employee because most NASA engineers worked with the same zeal and commitment that resembled the contractors. Contractors told jokes about how the contractors worked harder than the NASA employees, but the reality is that the responsibilities and functions of the NASA employees were different by design. The contractor jobs were established to reduce the number of federal workers in a theory that the cost of doing business would be reduced. That of course is a fantasy of economics because in 1980 some of the contractors were paid $48 per employee work hour, plus overtime, plus large quarterly bonuses. NASA employees were only making about $6 to $28 per hour with no bonuses except for management. The taxpayers were duped again. It is rarely cheaper to have contractors conduct federal work. Just imagine how costly the military would be if the soldiers, airmen, marines, and sailors were all contract employees with union memberships. It is likely that contractors provide the products and services more quickly or with better quality, but usually not cheaper.

Regardless of the tedium of the job, the space program workers at KSC tenaciously got the job done.

Even during the greatest setbacks in Space Shuttle hardware testing or schedule changes, the Space Shuttle Program team focused on the new goals and continued the procedures to quality completion. Quality was the main thrust of coming to work each day. Without a commitment to quality work, we would have better served the taxpayers not to have been on the job. That work environment was contagious. My colleagues taught me many worthy lessons and assisted me whenever I was exhausted.

The space hardware development activities of Russia, Japan, China, or Korea never distracted the Space Shuttle Program workers. We felt that NASA had the best space exploration workers in the world, and we were focused on working to the best of our abilities and endurance. Our concentration on the near-term program goals, and the lifestyle of quality production, were the same energies that propelled the nouveaux technologies of the Space Shuttle system into Earth orbit flight after flight with world record-setting successes.

During some of the lengthy countdowns of Space Shuttle launches, we had discussed whether our Russian equivalents in rocket science were as thrilled for our space exploration accomplishments as we hoped they would be. Our American achievements were not ones of jealousy or spite, but rather of progressing the world's knowledge of space travel and providing explorers a stable and reliable platform on which to conduct their research and observations of the Universe. The American space workers, while very proud of our own successes, hoped for peace amongst the many flags of all countries so that we could actually share our discoveries with each other and fully realize the awesomeness of this Universe and how delicate our existence truly is. Our national pride was exciting, but we did realize that our human-generated divisions prevent the world from realizing the maximum that exploration has to offer.

Politics is a world of its own that regularly attempts to control exploration, but in the end, the natural human fascination with exploration and discovery prevail over the whims of politics. The Human Race will have matured to a level of cooperation for which we can all be thankful when we can explore the Universe together, as a planet of diverse people, even during times of international conflict. It was my honor and privilege to have worked with so many people at KSC who also shared this vision of the Universe. We gave our best efforts with the resources that we had. The people of the United States developed The Space Shuttle Program and humbly placed a new chapter of science, engineering, and exploration history in the history book of the Universe. NASA earned the recognition as the best space exploration team of the last 42 years of the last century of the second millennium, A.D.

CHAPTER 11

THE INVESTIGATION:
THE LAST JOB OF NASA?

When a federal agency such as NASA suffers an accident, a defeat, or political turbulence, an investigation usually results. The people possess the right and privilege to have experts and unbiased investigators discover and recommend a course of action to preserve the NASA agency for the intent described in the U.S. Constitution. The experts and investigators may also make recommendations for adjusting or streamlining the agency actions, or even augment the agency charter under public laws.

The *Challenger* investigation was massive in scope. There were unlimited, diverse resources from NASA engineering, science labs, and various non-government consultants. Additionally, many other government and private labs were employed to analyze and solve numerous problems in the process of investigating.

I had lost daily contact with many of my colleagues due to my shrouded duty station at the Logistics Facility. However, I did work very closely with many other dedicated NASA engineers and Astronauts. During the most trying times, we sometimes meet people who inspire us because of their devotion to the work at hand. I was associated with several such people during the *Challenger* investigation. Dick Covey, a Space Shuttle pilot, saw nightmarish events at the Port Canaveral Navy dock where *Challenger* debris was brought ashore. Covey coordinated the transfer of the *Challenger* debris to the Logistics Facility.

Later in 1989, he would be the Pilot for the Return To Flight of the Space Shuttle Program on the STS-26 flight of *Discovery* with the redesigned SRBs.

Another inspirational person was Lt. Colonel Bryan O'Connor, Space Shuttle Commander, who was in charge of *Challenger* wreckage retrieval operations at KSC. Lt. Colonel O'Connor had been with the Marines as chief test pilot at Patuxent River, Maryland, for the evaluation of the *Harrier* jump jet. In 1993, seven years after the *Challenger* crash investigation was completed, I was requested by NASA Headquarters in Washington, DC to consult with the NASA Office of General Counsel and Lt. Colonel O'Connor regarding a Freedom of Information (FOIA) problem that was about to become a lawsuit in U.S. Federal District Court: *The People of the United States vs. NASA*. The legal problem was related to the *Challenger* wreckage photos and videos. At that time, Bryan was the Deputy Associate for Space Flight. Lt. Colonel O'Connor and I had many conversations that week about various areas of improvements in the Space Shuttle systems design that were still needed.

Mary Cleave, NASA Mission Specialist Astronaut, flew her first mission before the tragic 51-L Mission launch. Her specialty is in environmental engineering and sciences, and she was the Astronaut assigned to work with me for three days in the Crew Module wreckage area to confirm and verify all the dozens of instrument switch positions in the Flight Deck of the *Challenger.* It was very emotional and frightening for an Astronaut, who had already flown aboard a Space Shuttle with poorly designed field joints, to look close-up at the wreckage of the *Challenger's* Flight Deck. Astronauts who worked with the crash investigation realized that any one of them could have been assigned to the 51-L Mission. Mary never showed any sadness in front of me from the time she walked into the Crew Module debris until the time our three days of switch position work was complete. She seemed to be trying to digest the horror and disbelief.

As the investigation progressed over the many weeks, public and private hearings were being held in Washington, DC and at NASA centers around the country. The *Rogers Presidential Commission* was conducting the investigation hearings. There were many famous people on the Commission, such as Neil Armstrong, first man on the Moon; Chuck Yeager, first man to fly faster than the speed of sound; and Dr. Richard Feynman, physicist and Nobel Prize recipient in Physics. William Rogers was the Secretary of State during U.S. President Richard Nixon's Administration. President Ronald Reagan appointed William Rogers as leader for the *Rogers Presidential Commission* to investigate and make recommendations to the President to correct any problems found with the Space Shuttle Program.

Dr. Sally Ride, the first American woman to fly into space, was on the Commission. Sally flew as a Mission Specialist aboard the STS-7 Mission, and she was married to the Mission Specialist Astronaut and astronomer Dr. Steven Hawley who was also working the investigation. One day at the Launch Control Complex (LCC) at KSC, I was with Steve as we watched part of one of the *Challenger* investigation public hearings that was broadcast from Washington. Steve was saying words of encouragement out loud to the television image of his wife as she fired off a line of questions to the person on the witness stand who was under sworn oath. Steve was proud of Sally's efforts to get the exact facts that caused this Tragedy.

Those public hearings made the witnesses extraordinarily nervous. Imagine, a conservative engineering manager, under oath, on the witness stand, on worldwide television, being asked very direct, intimidating, and possibly incriminating questions. That was pressure.

There were two managers from my division (Mechanical Division) who were subpoenaed to testify, under oath, before the *Rogers Presidential Commission* and the American people. One of those managers was Bob Lang, a NASA propulsion engineer since the *Apollo* Program. Lang became the new Mechanical Division Chief a short time before the *Challenger* Tragedy. It was a difficult time to become chief of the division that contained a branch responsible for handling, stacking, and retrieving the Solid Rocket Boosters.

I have always believed that in government service a public servant whether employed, elected, or appointed, dutifully inherits situations created by servants who served before. Lang had a "VIP" invitation to testify before the *Rogers Presidential Commission* at the session held at KSC in March 1986.

The Commission was at KSC to inspect the facilities used to process the Space Shuttles, interview NASA and contractor employees, and review Space Shuttle processing procedures. The Commission also heard testimonies from specific managers who were responsible for the particular areas of interest, or who had a particular role in the decision to launch *Challenger.*

Lang went to the Visitor's Center at KSC called *Spaceport USA* to testify in the *Galaxy Theater* there. This theater is in the same building as the popular *I-Max Theater*. All engineers of the Mechanical Division heard that Lang would be testifying about the SRB stacking procedures. We could not imagine how he would become familiar so quickly with the SRB subject that is very complex. A person cannot become an SRB processing engineer overnight. We watched to see just how bad the testimony would be, or how great Lang could cope with the tough interrogation.

As you might have imagined, the *Rogers Presidential Commission's* intense interrogation was ferocious like a hungry Florida alligator and seemed to eat Bob Lang alive—complete with a scolding from the Commission Chairman, William Rogers, who mandated that no one will come before the Commission unprepared or misleading the Commission. Lang came back to the office frustrated, embarrassed, and his tie loosened. Lang said to us, "Man! I did the best I could." What a terrible situation he was in even though he had no responsibilities in the 1970s with the SRB design and assembly procedures during the SRB design and qualification phase.

The Commission also interrogated Charlie Stevenson, another NASA engineering colleague of mine. Charlie was a quiet, productive, and experienced rocket engineer who was somewhat shy in his personality. Charlie had successfully worked the *Nike* Rocket Program, the *Apollo* Program, and was now working with the Space Shuttle. In the Space Shuttle Program during 1986, Charlie was the Section supervisor for the External Fuel Tank of the Space Shuttle. He always knew extreme details about his areas of responsibilities and was in control. During times of engineering troubles Charlie would have at least two of his top engineers working on the problem.

Many times, Charlie and I engineered some remarkable feats of technology and psychological influencing. In 1991, Orbiter *Discovery's* belly had cracked hinge fittings of the Orbiter/ET umbilical doors. You might recall that the Space Shuttle *Discovery* was rolled back from the Pad to properly repair those hinges before flying. NASA had already given the go-ahead to launch, but had to reverse that decision to roll back to the VAB and OPF. I led the effort to provide the NASA Administrator with the accurate details of the hinge cracks and the consequences if the Space Shuttle was launched in that condition.   NASA Division-level managers were mis-reporting facts about the design problems with the hinge fittings of the Orbiter-ET umbilical doors. Charlie was supportive in helping me to deliver that new information to NASA Headquarters and NASA Administrator, Admiral Dick Truly. Admiral Truly realized the severity of the problem with the *Discovery* and he reversed the decision to launch. The Administrator was very angry with the NASA management for failing to correctly brief him on the severity of the cracked hinge fittings. We prevented a crash of Space Shuttle *Discovery*, STS-39, that would have certainly occurred during reentry over the Pacific Ocean.

The focus of the *Rogers Presidential Commission's* interrogation of Charlie was to examine the facts regarding duties and performance of the NASA Ice Team on the day of the 51-L launch, and to hear the findings from the photo analysis of the launch support cameras that were in place at Pad B. The ground-based cameras included manned and unmanned camera sites. The launch film of *Challenger* 51-L was removed from those cameras and taken south of the

This effort to ensure a safe Space Shuttle design is an example that if the management system is not succeeding in doing the job correctly by the rules, the workers must get the job done.   NASA and my country's form of government (freedom) allowed Charlie and me to ensure that the STS-39 *Discovery* flight was safe.

space center to Patrick Air Force Base to the photo lab for processing and printing. Charlie and one of his most trusted engineers, Greg Katnick, were in charge of the photo analysis efforts at KSC. In his briefcase, Charlie had a surprise for the Commission as he testified. The Commission was unaware of what Charlie was about to unveil on world television.

It is important to know that the *Rogers Presidential Commission* had a ground rule that no surprises would be exposed on television without the Commission being briefed on it before airtime. Charlie either did not know about that rule, or Charlie politely ignored the rule. I think I know which of the two possibilities it was.

Charlie had an 8 in. x 10 in. glossy photo of the failing SRB field joint as viewed from the famous north camera site. That camera site was special because its viewing angle provided a direct view of the suspected area of the right hand SRB that had failed beginning at SRB ignition when the internal pressure of the SRB spiked.

Charlie referred to the "puffs of black smoke" coming out of the SRB field joint of the right SRB. William Rogers and his Commission were surprised and baffled at the revelation of the puffs of smoke. Rogers inquired further for Charlie to clarify which puffs of black smoke he was referencing. With a boyish, "I got you" grin, Charlie pulled the photo from his briefcase and held it up for the world to see for the first time. Rogers took off his reading glasses and held them in one hand as he squinted to make an effort to absorb and believe what he was seeing. The puffs of black smoke that were shown jetting from the SRB side casing were proof that the SRB had failed at ignition on the Pad. The *Challenger* could have exploded on the

Pad. That would have killed the crew, destroyed the vehicle, and would have destroyed at least one launch Pad. That would have crippled the launch capabilities of the Space Shuttle Program because there are only two heavy-duty launch Pads for the Space Shuttle, Pads A and B.

Replacement of the Space Shuttle launch Pads if they were destroyed would be technically feasible, but the financial loss could sum into the billions of dollars, for three reasons.

First, the ability of NASA to support the launch schedule of four Space Shuttles would be severely affected. The loss of a launch Pad would cut in half the capability to conduct on-Pad test and checkout of the Space Shuttle integrated to the Pad systems. This lack of parallel processing would slow down the launch rate and create expensive backlogs of work. In turn, this would produce new expenses for NASA and launch customers who would have to pay storage and ground maintenance costs for their payloads that could not be installed and tested in the Space Shuttle on the Pad. The additional costs would soar into the hundreds of millions of dollars.

Second, the design, construction, and testing costs to replace a Space Shuttle launch Pad would be much more expensive than the original costs from the decade of the 1960s because of the different financial culture of business today. Today's businesses tend to have much more overhead than did contractors of the *Apollo* Program era. Even with inflation factored into the equation, the replacement costs would soar to painful levels to the taxpayers.

Finally, a Space Shuttle explosion on the launch Pad would likely damage the neighboring Space Shuttle Pad that is a mile or so away. A Space Shuttle explosion on the launch Pad would be very powerful and could propel massive pieces of steel and concrete toward the other Pad. The explosive shock wave could also be a source of damage at the other Pad.

The Rogers Presidential Commission visited KSC for that public hearing and the Commission members toured the various Space Shuttle processing facilities. The schedule and route of the Commission's inspection and fact-finding tour included whatever the members wanted to see. The Commission looked at nearly everything at KSC. They scrutinized paperwork, labs, ground and flight hardware, facilities, launch control support complexes, and interviewed people.

Particular attention to detail was given to the process, hardware, procedures, and people involved with the vertical stacking of the SRB segments upon the Mobile Launch Platform (MLP) inside the VAB. The Commission members saw everything in Complex 39 associated with processing a Space Shuttle for launch and landing. They were amazed at all that was involved with integrating, testing, and launching and recovering a Space Shuttle.

Greg Katnick and his photo analysis team had done an excellent job in producing and analyzing several hundred 8 in. x 10 in. photos of the *Challenger's* 51-L flight. One day, I was called away from the Crew Module wreckage area to go to Complex-A (where my actual office was) to inspect the photos of the 51-L launch.

I walked into the foyer of the Mechanical Division Chief's office and turned left to walk to the door that led to a small conference room about 20 ft. x 30 ft. of area. I knocked on the door and Greg Katnick said, "Come in." I entered and was stunned at what I saw. There were photo boards completely lining the walls of the conference room with about one hundred 8 in. x 10 in. color photos of the *Challenger* from engine start sequence through water impact in the Atlantic Ocean. This display was shocking, sad, and horrific. I took a deep breath and exhaled. Those photographs were the most sought-after photographs in the world at that time.

The photo quality was dramatic and revealing. The colors were vivid and the resolution of the images was crisp and clear. The photos seemed to be endless. They just wrapped around the room and the fluorescent lights illuminated them. The array looked clinical, like in a medical office, not soft as in a photo gallery.

Greg Katnick acted as if nothing was unusual about this room. The photos were color prints and the tempering shock experience made them seem black and white for a few seconds. The still photos were sequentially arranged from left to right and gave the illusion of a video replay of the crash. The room seemed to entrap me, wrapping me up in a vine of horrific photos. Greg asked me to look at the photos and determine anything that may indicate problems or phenomena with the Space Shuttle vehicle. It took a few minutes, but I adjusted to the task at hand. I commented on the flickering translucent glow that occurred at the base of the External Tank. We had seen that phenomenon on previous Shuttle flights, but we did not want to ignore it on this catastrophic flight. As the weeks passed by, the flickering glow phenomenon was eliminated as a source of any problems for the *Challenger*.

From the photos, I could study, up close, the failed right SRB field joint and the flame that had erupted through the steel SRB casing. One photo that was particularly shocking and revealing was the one that showed the Crew Module, which contained the Astronauts, flying through the sky like a bullet, seconds after the initial breakup of the Space Shuttle, with an SRB flying from left to right, directly in front of the Crew Module windows. I'm sure that the crew was anguished and frightened when they looked out through those Orbiter windows and saw the SRB flying in front of them, out of control.

I will always be an engineer who believes that all manned space launch vehicles should have an escape system designed into the vehicle from the beginning of the design phase. It has been tragic that the Space Shuttle design is without a true <u>escape</u> system. We engineers argued for such a system but were largely ignored. A perfect machine does not exist. Superb spacecraft design and planning should always include a method and a procedure to escape catastrophic events.

I used those dramatic crash photos of *Challenger* on several occasions to help verify and confirm our findings at the debris investigation site. I always attempted to find three or more substantiating data or evidence to conclude a theory as fact in the vehicle breakup analysis.

I had been in the conference room with the photos for about two hours. The *Rogers Presidential Commission* came by to see the photos and to have a meeting with the managers of the Vehicle Engineering Directorate. The room was too small for all the photos and people too. The Commission Chairman, William Rogers, accidentally broke the vertical tail and rudder off of the Space Shuttle model that we had in that conference room. His backside hit the tail of the model as he was trying to squeeze by to inspect the photos. That was a $40,000 engineering model that we were not supposed to touch. Rogers broke it with his butt.

The Chairman was very embarrassed and simply said, "Oh I'm sorry. I didn't mean to break the Shuttle." What I saw and heard was so paradoxical the chief accident investigator apologizing for breaking our model of the Space Shuttle. We were having a very weird year.

A few days later, Ron Phelps directed me to go over to an Air Force hangar across the Banana River to inspect the actual pieces of the failed sections of the right SRB steel casing that had been retrieved from the ocean. I drove the government car to the hangar that was secured by armed guards.

I was cleared to enter the hangar and I walked in. On the concrete floor were remnants of the SRB's steel casings about 200 square feet in area. Those steel pieces appeared pitiful, nearly flat in shape. Imagine a hollow cylinder of steel fractured into large pieces. The propellant had been burned away and the insulator material located between the steel casing and the propellant was exposed.

The melted section of the SRB steel casing was melted very irregularly. I carefully ran my finger along the sharp, jagged edge of the casing. The exact failure point of the SRB was on the tip of my right index finger. It was amazing how much *Challenger* wreckage had been recovered. Those pieces contained the chemical and physical secrets about the breakup sequence of *Challenger.*

So many of the events that transpired during the *Challenger* investigation seemed as if they were created in a nightmare. One example was when the General Purpose Computers (GPCs) of the *Challenger* were recovered from the Atlantic Ocean floor and brought to the Logistics debris area on another NASA flatbed truck.

The GPCs were the computer brains of *Challenger*. There were four primary GPCs that were programmed with the same software. The computers operated with what was called a "voting" concept. If one of the four GPCs computed an answer, state, or value that was different from the other three GPCs, the three computers in agreement voted to believe their value rather than the apparent erroneous value of the fourth computer.

The fifth GPC was called the Back-Up Flight Software (BFS) computer. The BFS computer contained software to get the Space Shuttle safely into orbit and through reentry in the extremely remote event that the four primary GPCs simultaneously failed. Thus far, four GPCs simultaneously failing has never occurred.

An undamaged GPC volume was similar to the equivalent volume of two standard concrete blocks placed end-to-end. The GPCs were mounted in *Challenger* in Avionics Bays 1 and 2, located in the forward section of the Mid Deck of the Crew Module. The damaged *Challenger* GPCs had been crushed flat from the topside toward the bottom side. The thickness of the damaged GPCs had been reduced to about five inches.

One day just before I left to go home after a hard day's work at the debris area, Ron Phelps told me that the next day a Lockheed C-141 Starlifter cargo aircraft would arrive at KSC at the Shuttle Landing Facility. It was to fly the *Challenger* GPCs to IBM Corporation in New York for failure analysis and digital data retrieval from the GPC memory locations.

As I drove through the space center on my way home, I was wondering why NASA needed a C-141 cargo aircraft to transport five crushed, smelly GPCs to IBM. The next day, when I arrived at the Logistics

Facility, I found out why C-141 aircraft was at the SLF. The security of a military transport was selected to ensure secure transport of the Orbiter GPC computers to IBM. At the POL area of the Logistics Facility there was a huge, white NASA tanker trailer with thousands of gallons of de-mineralized water. There was a large, rust-colored, rubber hose at the rear of the tanker with a lever action nozzle on the end. There were five bright blue, plastic 55-gallon hazardous waste recycling drums with removable lids.

Ron Phelps told me that my job that day was to fill the five drums with de-mineralized water nearly to the top, but leave enough space for one GPC to fit into each drum without over-spilling the water. After loading each GPC into its drum, the lid was to be secured and the appropriate codes and tracking information was to be attached as a bill of lading.

It seemed that whatever was controlling this surreal disaster was trying to see how much I could tolerate before I cracked. I couldn't believe that I was submerging crushed Space Shuttle GPCs in water in a drum for the cross-country flight aboard an Air Force cargo plane. I felt as if I were a mime in a strange play. The tasks were too unexpected and too contrary to our dreams, ambitions, and efforts of daily space center work.

I was tired and I was beginning to feel the real stress of all that had happened to us as space workers since the *Columbia* countdowns that began in November of 1985. What a strange and emotionally exhausting year 1986 had been. My feelings about the Tragedy, the loss of my friends' lives, the mistakes made by the SRB program managers at Marshall Space Flight Center in Alabama, and the entire bureaucracy were beginning to change. Who wouldn't become stressed out with all this insanity and unpredictable events happening continuously—without a break—not even a weekend off from work?

We pressed on with our duty as investigators, and as a commitment to our fallen Star Voyagers to find the causes of their demise, and to try to ensure all of us that a Tragedy like this would never happen again.

We loaded the blue plastic drums onto a NASA truck with a short flatbed and drove the pickled GPCs to the Shuttle Landing Facility (SLF) where the C-141 cargo aircraft was waiting. The drums were loaded and secured aboard the C-141. A short time later, the *Challenger* GPCs made their last flight home to the NASA contractor and all the people at IBM who created the GPCs with NASA computer software engineers. It seemed appropriate and respectful that the inanimate "brains" of the *Challenger* should return to the creative workers at IBM who conceived the design and built them.

I had organized and reconstructed the three levels of the Crew Module (Flight Deck, Mid Deck, and Lower Bay) under the POL carport area in the following manner: The Flight Deck and payload operations on-orbit workstation were located in the southern half of the carport structure. Military olive tarps shrouded the debris from view. The northern half of the POL carport structure was where I located the Mid Deck and Lower Bay. Also included in that area was the Orbiter's Airlock, which is a double-door compression/decompression cylinder used by Astronauts who exit the Orbiter for spacewalks. The three and one-half avionics bays, and their shelves (Avionics Bays 1,2,3A, and 3B) were also located in this section of the facility with the Mid Deck.

Imagine looking down toward the concrete floor

of the POL carport if you were hovering above. We laid out the Crew Module debris in the same configuration dimensionally as an undamaged Crew Module, except that the sidewall pieces were folded outboard and laid flat on the concrete floor. Imagine a three-dimensional Crew Module, split open lengthwise at the upper roof, and folded outboard.

Metal and plywood shelves were made in a configuration like the avionics bay shelves. After electrical avionics computers were recovered from the ocean, we placed the computers onto the shelves using a forklift. Some of the avionics computer shelves from the Orbiter were three, four, or five boxes to a section and weighed hundreds of pounds. The compressive, hydrodynamic loads on the Crew Module from the water impact in the Atlantic caused the avionics bays to become compressed. The extreme inertial loading from the acceleration of the massive computers on the aluminum shelves caused the shelves of the avionics bays to fracture into sections about one to three feet in length.

The shelves of the Crew Module avionics bays were typically designed to have avionics computers attached above and below the same shelf structure. This concept reduced the number of shelves required to support the computers necessary for an Orbiter. Some boxes were mounted on the top of a shelf and some were mounted on the underside of that same shelf. The fractured avionics shelves sometimes contained five avionics computer boxes, three computers on the top, and two on the bottom of the shelf.

The Orbiter's floor structural aluminum honeycomb panels of the Flight Deck and Mid Deck were fractured into sections of about two square feet. All of the attach points of the seats that were part of the floor panels were still intact. The seat mounts did not fail.

The seats sustained frame distortions and impact damage from other Crew Module components that fractured and struck the seats. All of the lap and upper torso restraint harnesses (seat belts) were sheared in tension on the right hand sides for all seven seats due to water impact inertial loads.

All control panels and lighting assemblies were broken free from their mounting structures and remained as loose items. All individual electrical components such as small voltage regulators, inverters, electrical ballast units, etc. were also broken free.

The Waste Containment System was broken into about a dozen pieces. The Crew Module side hatch, or entry door, was fractured into about a dozen pieces. The high quality optical window located on that hatch was destroyed on water impact.

All of the stainless steel potable water and waste water storage tanks, the Environmental Control and Life Support System (ECLSS) components that were located in the Lower Bay, below the Mid Deck, were disconnected from their mounting provisions and impacted, crushed, or ruptured due to water impact forces. The ECLSS components consisted of such items as the Lithium Hydroxide (LiOH) canisters that removed carbon dioxide from the breathing air, water separators that controlled air humidity, fans, and various controls and components.

Located at the upper section of the Orbiter's Mid Deck were the three Inertial Measurement Units (IMUs) that sense and measure the Orbiter's roll, pitch, and yaw rotational motion values and rates. Also located in the nose were the two optical navigation sensors, the Star Trackers. The Star Trackers are positioned 90

degrees from each other and provide navigation verification and updates to the guidance computers by
looking for specific stars in space.   GPCs, the flight
guidance computer program, and Star Tracker electro-
optical position reference "eyeballs" all work together
with the three IMUs to maintain and control the flight
dynamics required for all Space Shuttle flight operations
during the missions.   All three IMUs were damaged
with the port (left side) IMU being crushed the most as
well as the two Star Trackers that were located adjacent
to that left side IMU (IMU No. 1).   That crushing pattern
of the components was a revealing record of the attitude, or orientation, of the Crew Module at the moment
of water impact.

In aerodynamics, a "stagnation point" is a point
or a line about which fluid molecules have to go either
left, right, up, or down.   For example, as a rocket pene-
trates the atmosphere, air must move from the tip of the
nose cone and flow along the rocket's side.   The point
on the nose where the flow directional change occurs
is the stagnation point.

The stagnation point of the Crew Module as the
module impacted into the ocean water was located at
the forward, upper left quadrant of the Crew Module
assembly, between two of the windows located on the
Flight Deck just in front of the Commander's position
(Windows Nos. 1 and 2).

The entire Crew Module fractured like an
eggshell except that the Crew Module was cracked into
hundreds of pieces that ranged in size from chips of
paint to structural pieces in the avionics bays weighing
a couple of hundred pounds.   The investigation
revealed that the Crew Module was completely intact
until the moment of impact into the Atlantic Ocean.
The Crew Module was designed with an outer forward

fuselage to protect the Astronauts from meteor impacts while in orbit around the Earth. Several inches below that outer shell the Crew Module pressure vessel is located. The design concept is a shell within a shell.

Evidence indicated that all of *Challenger's* windows were intact prior to impact with the Atlantic Ocean. After water impact, the windowpanes and their window frames were severely fractured into small pieces of glass about the size of a dime or less. The titanium window frames that supported the panes separated from the aluminum pressure vessel that was simultaneously fractured into small pieces of aluminum alloy.

The Crew Module hit the ocean in a vertical position, slightly yawed to the right, and pitched slightly nose down with a negative pitch angle that made the nose tucked under. That is why the stagnation point was near the Star Trackers just forward of the number two forward window on the left of centerline.

There was evidence that the titanium window frames had made forceful impact through the seat back padding of the Pilot's seat (right seat). All of the overhead control panels, the center pedestal console controls, and the main forward instrument panel displays and controls were separated from the mounting structures. As in many crashes of aircraft, the instruments and gauge marks could possibly indicate final values before breakup. However, that evidence is a highly unreliable source to conclude any real finding without other confirmed sources of data. The Crew Module instruments lost electrical power at the initial breakup of the Space Shuttle prior to the impulsive forces of water impact.

The investigation concluded that the Crew Module did not receive any known penetrations that could have prompted the loss of cabin pressure. Cabin pressure is normally operated at 14.7 pounds per square inch in the Crew Module. Even the "watermelon" shaped stainless steel tanks in the Lower Bay, below the Orbiter's Mid Deck, did not come loose until water impact. During water impact, the stainless steel water lines that routed from the tanks, toward the rear, and attached to the rear pressure bulkhead, pulled out their steel mounting fittings that stabilized the lines and aluminum pressure bulkhead from relative bending. These two or three holes that were made at water impact were only about two to six square inches in area total. That was not large enough to allow for rapid de-pressurization of the Crew Module at altitude, even if the holes had been made at altitude. Since the holes in the pressure bulkhead were made at water impact, the holes could not have been a cause for in-flight decompression of the Crew Module.

The 27,000 pound Crew Module had a freefall speed of 207 miles per hour at water impact. Prior to impact, there was no contact with any significant debris that could have ruptured the pressure vessel. The bullet-shaped Crew Module had a low-drag coefficient and was ejected from the debris field in the sky before additional damage could be done to the module.

During the first seconds of the Orbiter breakup, there was a very brief "spike" of acceleration at about twelve times the force of gravitation, or twelve g's, that was directed up the vertical axis of the seats toward the top of the Crew Module. Twelve g's was not enough in force and duration to harm the crew physiologically. The Crew Module rose in altitude from 43,500 feet to 62,300 feet and then turned back toward the Earth in a ballistic freefall to the ocean. The bullet-like shape of the Crew Module provided for stabilized guidance during freefall and thus had little to no tumbling. The freefall was stable like a cone-shaped paper water cup being tossed up into the air and coming down to the ground point-first. The reason for describing this dynamic motion is to show that the Astronauts could have bailed out, or jumped, from the freefalling Crew Module if there had been parachutes and pressure suits available to them. The Astronauts could have walked away, alive and healthy, from the Tragedy.

There was virtually no damage to the Crew Module after the initial breakup of the Space Shuttle. Inside the Crew Module, electrical power was lost, no cabin air was recirculated, and there was certainly no way to control the attitude and flight dynamic motion of the ballistic freefalling Crew Module with the Astronauts aboard. Our collective evidence indicated that the Astronauts were alive during the freefall. This country should never again require Astronauts to suffer the indignity of flying high performance rockets into space without an ethically correct and humane escape system. I am not referring to an "egress" system, or a "bail-out" system, or an ejection system, but an "escape" system. An escape system provides a rapid escape from the catastrophic event to safety and recovery. All of the other bailout concepts get the people out of the vehicle only to contend with the chaotic environment outside the exploding or out-of-control vehicle.

The Crew Module weighed about 27,000 pounds as it plunged toward the ocean. That weight was without the Forward Reaction Control System (FRCS) module of reaction control jets and thrusters located forward of the Crew Module windows. The Orbiter nose broke away from the Crew Module just seconds after initial breakup of the Space Shuttle. The aerodynamic forces that severed the FRCS module from the Crew Module were generated when the Crew Module zoomed ahead of the Orbiter debris field in the sky and pitched nose-down to a high angle of attack. The Astronauts were helpless to do anything but crash if they remained captive inside the Crew Module that was accelerating in freefall towards the ocean.

With all of these horrific events taking place in approximately two minutes and twenty seconds from breakup to water impact, the Astronauts remained in their seats, belted in for "safety." It is likely that a person may speculate, as do many others, as to why the Astronauts did not panic and try to leave their seats. But if you were in a vehicle that was freefalling from 62,300 feet towards water that reacts like concrete, would you attempt to jump without a parachute?

The so-called *"Challenger* Accident" could have been avoided if not for some people's fears of politics and position, if not for misjudgments and cowardice. Especially appalling are the people who brushed under the table all of the Problem Reports from several flights prior to 51-L when the SRB O-rings had primary seal blow-by of the hot gases from inside the SRB. The general public is still unaware that the Space Shuttle's SRB nozzles also have O-rings that had malfunctioned on many flights prior to the *Challenger* 51-L flight. The SRB *nozzle* O-ring issues are in addition to the SRB *field joint* O-ring issues. The original SRB design was plagued with an epidemic of malfunctions of the O-rings. Information about the O-ring malfunctions on earlier flights is contained in the *Rogers Commission Report to the President of the United States* and is now a public record.

It had become evident that the Astronauts never experienced lethal dynamic forces or environmental conditions during the freefall of the Crew Module to the Atlantic Ocean. The investigation revealed that at least two of the Astronauts were conducting a last resort procedure for breathing supplemental emergency oxygen as *Challenger* plummeted to the Earth.

Seated on the Flight Deck were the Mission Commander, Dick Scobee (left seat), the Pilot, Mike Smith (right seat), Mission Specialist El Onizuka (right rear seat behind Smith), and Mission Specialist Judy Resnik (center rear seat between and behind the two front seats). Resnik's seat in the Space Shuttle was what we called the "best seat in the house," since it provides a spectacular view of all six forward windows, the overhead windows, most displays and controls and the pilot's activities. The Astronaut in the center seat performs cockpit checklist bookkeeping duties like a flight engineer.

During the retrieval and inspection of thousands of pieces of debris from the Crew Module, four metal oxygen tanks with rotary valves were recovered. They were called Personal Egress Air Packs, or PEAPs, and were designed to provide an individual Astronaut with five minutes of breathing oxygen in the event of an evacuation from the Shuttle on the launch Pad during countdown. The PEAP tanks supplied oxygen into the Astronauts' custom-fit helmets. An evacuation from the Space Shuttle's Crew Module during a launch countdown could include hazardous gases outside of the Space Shuttle on the access arm, the Pad tower, the slidewire, the high-speed elevator, or the stairs. If an Astronaut were to become unconscious from breathing those hazardous gases, the fallen Astronaut would become a stumbling block to the other Astronauts who would be running along the same evacuation path.

The two PEAP tanks were not in bad condition

considering that they had been in a violent crash at water impact. The regulator valve on one tank had been bent and crimped so that whatever oxygen was in the tank at water impact was contained.

The regulator valve can only be rotated to initiate airflow from the tank. Linear impact inertial forces from the water impact could not have rotated the manual valve knob to initiate airflow. The rotated valve knob most likely had been activated by a crewmember. We believe that El Onizuka rotated the airflow regulator valve knob to initiate airflow for Smith, who sat in front of Onizuka. The oxygen tank was mounted to the back of Smith's seat and it appeared that Onizuka assisted Smith in this futile and last resort effort to survive.

We sent the PEAPs to labs for analysis to determine what gas was inside each tank, how many minutes of gas were left, and what caused the regulator valve stem to become bent. The test results were that the valve was bent from impact forces and that the rotary knob that activates the oxygen flow must have been turned to the "on" position by a crewmember. In one particular tank, there was approximately two minutes and twenty seconds of gas left in the tank. The ballistic trajectory and freefall of the Crew Module was about two minutes and twenty-six seconds until water impact. The freefall time added to the remaining time of the oxygen in the PEAP tank equals four minutes and forty-six seconds. This was fourteen seconds short of the five minutes total oxygen supply time available in the PEAP.

Analysis of the *Challenger* wreckage analysis provided NASA with an credible evidence that suggested what some of the Astronauts may have been doing after the Orbiter broke apart at 71-73 seconds into flight. Activation of the PEAPs during flight indicated that the Astronauts were hoping to survive by applying their instincts and training.

We can speculate forever about what the Astronauts experienced during flight. These well-disciplined men and women would have given every effort to fly to a safe end of mission. As the NASA investigation revealed, at least the pilot Astronauts were using what they had (the PEAPs) in order to attempt survival.

Many people from various government organizations became involved with the *Challenger* investigation. Very few people were authorized to view or work with the Crew Module debris. The list of people who were authorized to enter the guarded area included several Astronauts, a few NASA managers who were not involved with the decision to launch, about four NASA engineers, several contractor carpenters and heavy equipment operators, about six Lockheed technicians and quality inspectors, and Technicolor and Lockheed photographers. Other personnel authorized included National Transportation Safety Board (NTSB) investigators from Washington, DC, CIA and FBI agents, a few military officers from the U.S. Navy and U.S. Air Force, and two crash investigators from the U.S. Army in Fort Rucker, Alabama.

Most of the days in 1986, I worked in the Crew Module area about twelve to eighteen hours per day. Of all the people who inspected the Crew Module debris, the most memorable for me was the Chief of the Astronaut Office at JSC for NASA, Space Shuttle Commander John Young, who commanded STS-1, the first Space Shuttle flight.

I was told that John would be arriving 10 A.M. the next morning. About ninety percent of the Crew Module was reconstructed and the flight seats of the

Commander and Pilot were in position amongst the instrument panels. It was very upsetting to see the arrangement of Crew Module wreckage. Working day and night around the wreckage desensitized the investigators.

I considered the fact that my professional friend and hero, John Young, was coming to the site to see the reconstructed *Challenger* wreckage. John had been my role model in many ways. I was always inspired by his well-informed cockiness about his profession. John had the raw visage of a test pilot and the look of a man who had been to the Moon twice. I learned from the old timers of NASA that I was one of a few people who could get John to smile. We never saw him laugh out loud. All you had to do was to talk about the Orbiter, his mission, and ask him if he had fun flying that mission. That technique always prompted John to grin and tell his story.

John compiled information from the entire NASA team regarding the Space Shuttle design, new technologies, and problems that developed with the spacecraft. He has never been known for eloquence, but John has always stated what's on his mind in a manner that does not hurt others. Everyone knows what his position is on any topic. I admire that. The silent people who say what those at the top want to hear are the ones to worry about.

John was the first man to fly a Space Shuttle when STS-1 with the Orbiter *Columbia* was launched on April 12, 1981. He was the Pilot for Commander Gus Grissom of the first two-man launch, *Gemini* III, launched March 23, 1965. John served as Command Module Pilot of *Apollo* 10 to the Moon, launched May 18, 1969. Hungry for the feeling of being weightless and for exploration, John was the Commander of *Apollo* 16, launched April 16, 1972.

I was not sure what John's reaction to this mess of debris would be. I had concerns for his reaction to losing five of his full-time employees aboard the *Challenger* crash. I didn't know exactly what I would say to him. John was the closest person to the *Challenger* at the time of the vehicle breakup. He was flying Safety Chase and Weather Observations in the NASA Shuttle Training Aircraft (STA), which is a highly modified Gulfstream II.

John had arrived at the Logistics Facility and Ron Phelps called to inform me. John was cleared through the gate at the guard checkpoint and I escorted him to the Crew Module wreckage.

We were nervous about the imminent viewing of the *Challenger* debris. The nervousness was a similar feeling to that when you go to view a deceased person in a funeral home. John and I made small talk about the last time either of us had been back to the Georgia Tech campus and talked about a couple of professors we both had at Tech during different decades.   It seemed absurd of John to ask if I had been back to the campus in Atlanta, with all of the chaotic work that had been going on for months. When did I have time to visit?

As we approached the olive-colored military tarps that were the walls of the Crew Module debris area, we got quiet. We rounded the corner of the carport structure and walked directly into the section that contained the Crew Module Flight Deck. As we walked slowly through what was the Flight Deck of *Challenger,* John said nothing. After about ten minutes, he said, "It doesn't look as bad as I thought."

How could John say that? The Crew Module was a fractured menagerie of components that smelled of decaying barnacles. That wreckage was a nightmare from Hell. I wondered what he meant. The only thing I could imagine he meant was that the module had been fractured and not compressed flat; and that there was absolutely no fire in the Crew Module. Perhaps John wanted to see the features of the wreckage that suggest a survivable breakup sequence. Since there was no fire and no decompression, perhaps this type of accident is survivable with the proper escape system. Whatever John meant by his comment, I was growing to dislike these gruesome tasks that seemed to have no end.

Since 1986, many people have asked me if there was a cover-up of the truth and facts regarding the *Challenger* Tragedy and the investigation report. Whenever a catastrophic event occurs in our country that involves the federal government and tax money, there are always citizens and reporters who take the position of not believing what the government has said about the event. A distrust of government seems automatic. I'm glad that those skeptical people are in the world because they do provide a continuous check and balance. The public has largely believed the findings and recommendations by NASA and the *Rogers Presidential Commission* regarding the Space Shuttle vehicle destruction and the NASA Shuttle Program operations. NASA has a reputation for integrity and commitment to safety of flight. The *Challenger* Tragedy stressed the public to the limit of what they could technically absorb and emotionally accept regarding the trust and confidence of NASA.

Doubts or concerns about the truth and ethics of the investigation can, in large part, be answered from the *Rogers Presidential Commission Report on the Challenger Accident Investigation* (5 vols.). The investigation was structured with educated, experienced, wise, and good-hearted people who wanted the truth to be discovered, recorded and shared. Almost every investigator did their best work, were motivated by duty, possessed the drive to do the best work in space exploration, and were compelled to ethical work for respect to the deceased Astronauts. NASA's curiosity was at its peak to know everything about which Space Shuttle systems or components failed to perform during the 51-L flight.

There was one incident during the debris analysis in which there was an attempt by two NASA employees to bypass the investigation process. It involved an attempt to make false conclusions regarding the fate of the glass windowpanes of the Crew Module during the Orbiter breakup sequence in the sky. If the windowpanes had fractured from impact with debris in the sky, the cabin pressure would have been decompressed at the initial breakup altitude of 43,500 feet.

If that theory of decompression had occurred, it would have meant that the Astronauts would have lost consciousness from oxygen deprivation (hypoxia) and that their bodies and the objects inside the Crew Module would have shown decompression effects. The Astronauts would not have been able to use the PEAPs, since rapid decompression could have quickly killed them. If the Astronauts were unconscious or dead, they would not have experienced "pain and suffering" during the two-minute and twenty six-second freefall before the ocean impact.

With no "pain and suffering," the financial settlement from a lawsuit against NASA would be less money. Without revealing the names of those two NASA employees for legal reasons, I will say that they made an attempt to alter the analysis of the small fragments of the windowpanes that remained captive in the window support grooves of the window frames. The attempt to conduct a non-scientific analysis and publish that propaganda in a false report was not how NASA has historically operated.

I had already determined from my observations of the window frames and the small amount of window fragments that the windows were intact until water impact. We also had photos that clearly showed the flat panes of glass reflecting sunlight during the freefall. However, my initial study of the window system breakup sequence did not conclude the fate of the windows that were not in view of the tracking cameras. I could not be certain that the two Payload Bay viewing windows were not cracked or shattered during the vehicle breakup.

I needed a couple of more positive data points that would confirm either the presence of cabin pressure, or possibly the lack of cabin pressure if decompression had occurred. If decompression of the cabin atmosphere had occurred, objects inside the Crew Module that had the 14.7 pounds per square inch of pressure would have expanded, distorted, or ruptured from the difference in pressures from decompression.

Nothing. Nothing in the stowage lockers, galley, and other compartments were distorted from a decompression of the Crew Module. Additionally, the aluminum honeycomb panels of the Crew Module structures showed no evidence of decompression. There was no rapid decompression.

If any of the Crew Module pressure windows had fractured, then there would have been an extremely rapid decompression at an altitude above 43,500 feet. One person in particular asked me many questions regarding my report and finding that stated the position of Crew Module pressure not being decompressed. I had wondered why that person was asking so many questions and implying that my findings were erroneous.

Around late March of 1986, I was offered a weekend off for the first time since the Christmas break in December, 1985. I was pleased that I had two days off. I really needed the break. Those two days off seemed like a lengthy vacation because I was so tired from the grueling work schedule I had been keeping.

I departed from work at KSC at 2 A.M. on that Friday morning and drove to my home in Cape Canaveral for some very needed sleep. After awaking on that same day, I drove 435 miles to my mother's home in Augusta, Georgia.

I recall this episode to emphasize that a couple of NASA employees intentionally arranged for me to have the weekend off so that they could orchestrate their corrupt attempt of producing false reports regarding the Orbiter window analysis in hopes of submitting the report to the *Rogers Presidential Commission.*

I traveled back to the Cape and was at work the next Monday afternoon for the night shift at the Crew Module debris area. I had been at work for about two hours when Kelly Longhofer asked me if I had heard that someone had done a windowpane analysis while I was gone that weekend. Kelly was the quality inspector who worked with me every day in that insur- mountable task of identifying parts of the Space Shuttle.

I asked Kelly, "What analysis of the windows?" Kelly answered, "Some NASA people came to the Crew Module window frames, removed pieces of glass, and did an analysis. They wrote a memorandum (called an Avoid Verbal Order, or AVO) that says that all the windows failed in flight either by popping inward or outward."

I was stunned. I thought Kelly was joking with me. Quality inspectors have always joked with engineers. I thought Kelly was teasing me because I was the NASA window systems engineer.

Kelly told me where the AVO memorandum was located. I retrieved the AVO and read it. I was stunned to see that anyone in NASA would fabricate false data behind my back. That was a direct effort by a couple of NASA employees to lie to the people of America.

After thinking several hours about what action to take to stop that lie from being published or reported, I decided that two actions were necessary. Most importantly, I called an independent consultant named Dr. Suresh Gulati, a fracture mechanics scientist specializing in glass fractures and failures. Dr. Gulati worked at Corning Glass Works in Corning, New York. I requested that Corning send him to KSC to take window fragment samples and analyze them for fracture mechanics. He was world-renowned for his abilities to analyze fractured glass. I had the authority, as an investigator, to incorporate any professional assistance I needed that would help discover, develop, and find the truth about the vehicle breakup.

Dr. Gulati came to KSC several days later. About ten of us investigators were witnesses as he carefully removed, bagged, and identified the windowpane fragments. I made sure that the Technicolor photographer was present to photo-document the official window fragment sampling and identification. The glass pieces were taken back to Corning Glass Works and were analyzed.

The window failure findings were decisive and conclusive. The window failure analysis report from Corning Glass Works concluded that all of the Crew Module windows were catastrophically and totally destroyed due to extreme hydrodynamic forces caused by high velocity impact in the Atlantic Ocean. The attempt to misrepresent the evidence had been foiled.

As a secondary method to ensure that the truth about the Orbiter window system's performance would be truthfully reported to the people, I was fully prepared to go to the wire service reporters and recruit them to probe and correct any lie that could have been published. The efforts of those two wayward NASA employees to falsely represent the truth about the window failure sequence had been exposed and stopped. The culprits of the lie then accepted our findings that the windowpanes were intact and unbroken until water impact. What choice did those two have? The truth about the failure of the Crew Module windows was clear and obvious. The lie was too fantastic to make it resemble truth in the midst of so much good science being applied to the investigation. The integrity of one person compensates for dishonesty of many.

Many weeks had passed since the crash of *Challenger*. I had seen only a few of my colleagues in weeks. Those colleagues and most Americans were very curious as to whether there really was a large collection of "mangled Shuttle debris," as the Press had reported.

We investigators of NASA, and the NTSB consultants, listened and considered the curiosity of everyone regarding the proof of evidence for the cause of the crash. Lack of positive proof, or even probable cause, can lead to rumors, lack of faith, and erosion of trust for the investigation findings and recommendations. NASA felt that public was missing a piece to the puzzle of reality. The entire Tragedy had left the public in a dazed and surrealistic state of mind that needed closure. Had NASA truly lost a crew, a Space Shuttle, and a mission?

NASA decided to allow the Press into the Logistics Facility to photograph the Orbiter debris but excluded the Crew Module debris. *Challenger's* Crew Module was located inside a building that was separate from the main building where the fuselage and wings were located. That is, except for the rear pressure bulkhead of the Crew Module. Ron Phelps had forgotten to have the Crew Module relocated to the carport structure called the POL.

The Press got a piece of what they were salivating to photograph–a piece of the Crew Module! The rear pressure bulkhead was not supposed to be in the area where the fuselage was located. The sight of that bulkhead with the two Payload Bay viewing windows made the Press more curious, which led to speculation as to where the Crew Module was actually located. Uncertainty over its location drove those reporters crazy. Newspaper, radio, television, and wire services reporters were all clamoring to find the Crew Module wreckage.

Reporters asked me if I knew where the Crew Module was located. Those reporters did not know that I was working in the Logistics Facility analyzing the Crew Module wreckage. I reversed the role on the reporters by asking them where they had imagined it was. I told them, "A really good reporter would have already found the Crew Module investigation area." The late Mr. Jules Bergman, an *ABC* reporter, had the personality and style to have found the Crew Module first. Bergman was caught entering a restricted area while trying to gain access to the Hangar L facility where the autopsies were being performed on the Astronauts' remains. NASA then restricted Mr. Bergman's movements at KSC and Hangar-L.

The other reporters detested the idea that Bergman could scoop the location of the module. They probably could not imagine that NASA would shelter, in an outdoor carport facility with canvas walls, evidence as significant to the investigation as the Crew Module. Their expectations caused them to miss finding out its location.

The Logistics Facility was about 400 yards away from the Press Site at Complex 39. The reporters simply missed it. It was, however, impressive to see the enthusiasm of the Press corps. In 1986, it seemed to me that there was no other news that anyone cared to know.

There were two reporters who worked for *United Press International (UPI)* who had bet me a case of beer (to be chilled to 34°F) that even though I could not reveal to them the location of the Crew Module, they would find the module through their "vast network of sources and information." The Press never found the Crew Module. Bill Harwood and Rob Navias still owe me a very cold case of beer. Harwood now works for *CBS* radio, and Navias works for NASA, JSC Public Information Office.

The time came when all of the *Challenger's* recovered parts had been identified, logged, and photographed. The reconstructed Crew Module had been probed, sampled, moved, pondered upon by many minds, and generally used for the many purposes of crash investigation. Many facts had been learned about the vehicle failure and the crew actions and fate. The causes of the Tragedy had been verified, reported honestly, and a new direction for the future of NASA had been recommended.

We investigators were exhausted and emotionally drained. We had become changed people for the rest of our lives. We were much closer and had developed an enhanced appreciation for all of the resourceful people we had encountered.

Ron Phelps instructed me to produce videotaped documentation of all of the Crew Module debris prior to placing the wreckage in wooden crates for burial. Burial? What burial? NASA had made the decision to bury nearly all of the *Challenger* debris in two underground *Minuteman* Inter-Continental Ballistic Missile (ICBM) silos that were located near the ocean at the Cape Canaveral Air Force Station.

It was strangely sad that this eternal nightmare was nearing its end, or seemed close to its end. There was an excitement that reminded me of students' elation at the end of a school year–anxious for the end, but somewhat sad about the conclusion considering all that we had experienced together. Close emotional fellowships had been established during the chaos of those historic months.

Two television technicians from the Lockheed Audio/Visual group from the KSC Complex 39 Press Site were assigned to work with me at the Space Shuttle wreckage area. Fletcher Hildreth, or "Fletch" as we called him, was the camera operator, and was formerly employed by public television in Orlando, Florida. Fletch liked racing cars for sport. Fletch was a soft-spoken and intelligent camera operator and we worked well together during the videotaping. Rick Morris, a proud father and committed Christian, was the audio man who recorded the sound for the video. I had to wear dress clothes and a tie for the videotaping. I hadn't worn a tie to work in months. We were usually dirty as pigs while working at the debris area.

I had made photocopies of several Space Shuttle diagrams and mounted them on a board. The video

began by explaining the arrangement of the Space
Shuttle systems. Then, visually and aurally, I
explained the entire Crew Module debris that included
Flight Deck, Mid Deck, Lower Bay, bulkheads, wiring,
avionics boxes, the potty, the airlock, windows, and
displays and controls. Knowledge of the design,
construction, and failure analysis of the Space Shuttle
was crucial to the quality and communication of the
contents of the video.

We taped many hours of unedited videotape of
the Crew Module wreckage. The videotaping process
lasted a couple of weeks. As we taped in the morning,
the weather was typical gorgeous spring season
weather at the Cape. As each day progressed, the
usual Florida thunderstorms rumbled into the area and
we sometimes had to stop taping due to lightning.
Rick, Fletch, and I gave our best efforts to produce the
videos.

After days of taping, I had to spend a couple of
days at the video production studio reviewing the tapes
to check for errors or implications that may have been
classified or misleading. After the editing, the video
documentation task was finally over. I never saw those
Challenger tapes again until 1993 when NASA
Headquarters in Washington called me at my new job
with the Federal Aviation Administration. The NASA
Office of General Counsel asked me to consult them in
a legal case regarding NASA's denying a Freedom of
Information Act (FOIA) request for release to the
public of the Crew Module debris videotapes and
photos.

After editing the videotapes in that day in 1986,
I returned to work at the Crew Module debris area.
Ron Phelps said, "We need to box up all of the Crew
Module pieces." That would be quite a task. Most of

the investigation activities were very time consuming and this task was no exception.   Packing *Challenger* debris into the wooden crates continued for many days. After all the lids were sealed onto the crates of *Challenger* debris, we still had two wooden pallets of miscellaneous, unidentifiable parts.

Those two crates of junk looked pitiful sitting on the big empty concrete floors of the carport structure. They were like the "misfits" from a world of famous spaceships with no home to claim. We shoveled those loose pieces into the last crate and nailed the lid onto the crate. To the end, this episode of space exploration history was unbelievable and bizarre.

This investigation was now about seventy-five percent complete and involved the hardest, most demanding situations I've ever faced in my career. All the way through this necessary, miserable, yet captivating ordeal, I felt that the investigation might have been the last job that NASA would ever do in the manned space programs.   There were so many political elements to the space program and it was hard to imagine the U.S. Congress supporting us after this tragic mess.

CHAPTER 12

THE PAIN OF NASA

So often society views NASA as just a bunch of old rocket scientists, somewhat robotic or inanimate. That description is far from the case. Perhaps the NASA employees and contractors felt more pain than anyone over the *Challenger* Tragedy. We had to clean up the mess and attempt to find direction for the future of space exploration. The extensive NASA family felt many forms of pain during the Tragedy. Some of the NASA people were able to cope immediately. Other people, like the investigation team, had to delay the mourning and healing process, as the tedious, dirty work of crash investigation expanded.

The local Florida community was very understanding of NASA's trauma in 1986. Elders and youngsters were genuinely compassionate and they truly seemed to feel that NASA's losses were their losses. Children from near and far made pictures, sketches, poems, and prayers for the NASA workers. Businesses displayed signs with words of hope, prayers, and encouragement. Advertisements for making more money were unimportant in the local area for many months. Ministers at churches offered healing guidance about handling such desperate adversity. People who were normally unreasonable became more compassionate. The locals seemed to respect the work ethics and historical achievements of NASA.

I have no regrets about my work prior to or after the *Challenger* Tragedy. My responsibility was for Orbiter hardware. All of my systems worked per design specification for the 51-L flight. My feelings of pain were for the loss of my friends and colleagues of the *Challenger* crew, for the engineers who had made the unethical program management choices regarding the SRB design deficiencies, and for those who had failed in their responsibilities to correct those design problems.   My pain was for the legacy and spirit of the agency of NASA in the realization that the agency would never again possess the innocent reputation that it had enjoyed in the past.

After the crash, many of the space program employees had feelings of depression and guilt.   That was part of the healing process.   The vast majority of those people were blameless, though they were searching their souls for any way that they might have contributed to the Tragedy. They scrutinized their actions that led up to the launch to determine if they could have stopped the unsafe SRB design from being launched.   NASA Space Program workers always celebrated together, and that time we grieved together. NASA people from the decade of the 1970s and 1980s did not abandon each other in a time of despair. We grieved and healed ourselves back to the condition necessary for properly managing a space exploration program that requires standards beyond world-class.

As a crash investigator, I was in search of the causes of the breakup of the vehicle and other common causes and latent failures in the basic vehicle design.   The answers to my questions were contained in the wreckage. My job was to apply my knowledge and experience to accomplish my assignment of finding the answers in concert with the investigation team.   A single person could not do all the work that had to be accomplished. We investigators had to work as a trusting team and call upon experts in all areas from all around the planet. The investigation process was not like finding a needle in a haystack. Instead, it was more like finding the solutions to math word problems. We were in search of evidence that could be the values for the variables in the "equations" of what was wrong with the Space Shuttle design. As we investigators concluded later, the main problem with the Space Shuttle vehicle design was that a couple of NASA SRB engineering managers allowed the flawed SRB design to fly when they should have corrected the design problem in 1977, four years before the first launch (STS-1). What possessed those program managers to have allowed the original flawed design to fly twenty-five flights? That's infuriating!

The overall design of the Space Shuttle vehicles is quite sufficient for safe travel for a high performance vehicle. Many American aerospace workers have done marvelous work in design, manufacturing, and maintenance through the years to produce and maintain this remarkable flying machine. In mechanical design, it only takes one critical system failure to bring down a Space Shuttle, or even an entire Space Shuttle Program. The SRB critical system design flaw in the field joint, and the management cover-up of that unacceptable design, knocked the wings out from under the Space Shuttle Program. That "fall from the sky" diminished the excellent, exemplary reputation that NASA and its contractors had built over the years. What an awful shame for such an avoidable act to occur.

Kelly Longhofer, the Lockheed Quality Inspector, was a great friend and companion as we worked at the Crew Module wreckage area. One morning at about 10 A.M., we were attempting to relocate the wire bundles of the Crew Module from the three-sided outdoor bays to the carport structure where the main pieces of the Crew Module were located.

Miles of electrical cables were wound together like spaghetti with decaying barnacles that had begun to smell badly.

We thought that we could untangle the bundles and drag them by sections to the Crew Module area about 25 feet away. We discovered very quickly that this was much harder than it seemed at first. Those wire bundles were heavy. It seemed that they were fastened to the ground.

The dynamic Florida weather was in typical form that morning, and produced a powerful thunderstorm with so much rain that we called it a "gully washer." We had the first section of the wire bundles positioned in the area of the concrete driveway that was contoured for water drainage and was located between the bays and the carport structure. The flood of rainwater was about five inches deep and flowing fast.

Our white, cotton coveralls were soaked and we smelled like goats. We tugged and pulled on the mass of wire bundles as our shoes submerged in the rainwater. We slipped down as we pulled and strained as if we were in some sort of tug-of-war with the heavy mass of tangled electrical wires that had been the "nervous system" of a very wonderful and reliable spaceship. Emotionally and physically, I was at my limit of what I wanted to tolerate. I sat there with water soaking through my clothes, grasping the wire bundle in an attempt not to give up, and I just started crying from fatigue, sorrow, and the futility of the task. Then, after my brief cry, I realized that it seemed to me that there was nowhere to go except up. So, I got my soaking wet butt up and got to work. Kelly and I were at a low point and we needed encouragement and rest.

Kelly and I helped each other from the rainwater drainage and walked around to clear our minds. We agreed that we had never imagined we would ever be doing such a crazy job. We decided to use a fork-lift to move the wire bundles while being careful to avoid damage to the wires that could mask original damage from the crash.

We felt pain for the many top brass managers of NASA and contractors who were catching hell over the *Challenger* Tragedy, the design of the SRBs, and the flawed decision to launch. I have always disliked seeing leaders removed from their lofty positions simply because they are the stewards of the responsibilities to make sure that all goes well. However, leaders who deliberately conduct deceptive deeds should be removed from responsibility and justly punished.

Generally, NASA employees were going through the humiliation of the public viewing of the "dirty laundry" of technical and political elements of the agency. NASA's humiliation was broadcast around the world on television and radio. The public trust that had been developed over many years was being replaced with public doubt.

The investigation team was thankful to hear news reports of encouragement and prayers. We needed all the support we could get. During the investigation, so many kinds of people came into contact with one or more elements of the investigation. Included were Astronauts, politicians, law enforcement agents, legal representatives, technicians of every kind, consultants, and officials from other countries. They were either there to help, or they were just curious.

NASA is one of the best technical organizations that continuously record the day-to-day history of the activities of the agency as set forth by the *Title 42 of the*

Public Health and Welfare Codes. Did you get that? That's right. The basis of justification for the United States Congressional approval of the organization of NASA was under the laws of health and welfare. Very few American citizens know how NASA was conceived and empowered by law. The people who work at the offices of NASA Centers perform marvelous and comprehensive jobs of recording NASA's complex history.

Former President John F. Kennedy has received much credit and glory for his support of the manned space programs of *Gemini* and *Apollo*. However, the heavy work was done during the 1950s when former U.S. Army General Dwight D. Eisenhower was U.S. President. President Eisenhower, combined with leaders in the Senate such as Lyndon B. Johnson, built the framework of what became *Title 42 of the Public Health and Welfare Codes, Chapter 26 – National Space Program, Subchapter II – Coordination of Aeronautical and Space Activities, Sections 2472 and 2473*, the NASA charter.

America's premier aeronautical research and development organization prior to 1958 was the National Advisory Counsel on Aeronautics (NACA). NACA was most historic in measuring the parameters and behaviors of the Earth's atmosphere, defining aircraft wing airfoil cross-sectional geometric shapes, and capturing that physics in tables and catalogues. NACA was not under a public welfare program and was prolifically successful in providing new technologies. The technical and political work that established NACA and NASA happened before U.S. President Kennedy's Administration was elected. Those technicians, scientists, and engineers who, in the 1940s and 1950s, were the fathers and mothers of what is now NASA, earned a great amount of respect.

Not to be outdone, U.S. Senator and President Lyndon Johnson, orchestrated the move of about half of the manned space flight training and operations from what was called Cape Canaveral and then Cape Kennedy to the new Lyndon B. Johnson Space Center in Clearlake, Texas near Houston.   Johnson Space Center (JSC) is organizationally a more powerful space center than Kennedy Space Center.   Included in the move were the NASA Astronaut Office, Astronaut training, and the mission flight operations organizations that are now called Mission Control. Mission Control is responsible for the flight portion of the manned missions that are launched from Kennedy Space Center (KSC).   More significantly, Johnson Space Center is responsible and accountable to NASA Headquarters, Washington, for the Space Shuttle Program design, funding applications, and program management.

Each October, the U.S. Congress and the President decide how much money to appropriate and allocate to fund NASA programs.   The Congress (Legislative) and the Office of the President (Executive) struggle each year with the political question: Why should we use tax money to fly in space when we could feed a hungry child with that same tax money? Former Senator William Proxmire, Democrat from Wisconsin, was successful in ending the funding for the *Apollo* Program by arguing within the context of the *Title 42 of the Public Health and Welfare Codes*.   In 1972, three *Saturn V* rockets and their *Apollo* spacecraft had already been built and paid for when Congress, led by Senator Proxmire, ended the *Apollo* Program, one of the most successful scientific expeditions in the history of human life on Earth.

Congress ultimately approved Space Shuttle Program funding in 1972 after fighting a long and difficult battle with NASA and the U.S. Air Force. The U.S. Air Force has always been recognized for its political and scientific applications in support of NASA and the proposed Space Shuttle Program. Without the strategic and political support of the U.S. Air Force, NASA would not have won Congressional approval for the Space Shuttle and the capability to serve an Earth-orbiting International Space Station.

The U.S. Air Force, NASA, and welfare program proponents annually struggled and argued like sweaty Rugby football players over the insane begging for budgetary funding allocations. All three groups received money, and each group felt that they should have been allocated more money than they received. The facts are that welfare and health lost much of the money pie because NASA's Charter was in *Title 42 of the Public Health and Welfare Codes*. NASA lost much of the money pie because welfare and health were also in *Title 42*. The annual struggle between technology and welfare is contrary to the success of either program. Efficiency in budget allocation and authorization will only become reality for these three federal programs when NASA, health, and welfare function within their uniquely designed Federal Public Code. The massive quantities of money and time that have been wasted from this Public Code misalignment will continue as long as the taxpayers allow the process to continue. It is the taxpayer's money after all.

The U.S. Congress has continued to add more NASA agency requirements in the *Title 42* NASA Charter, and then has reduced the workforces of NASA. Efficiency and performance has declined during the 1990s as evidenced by the failed or lost space probes to the Moon, Mars, and to Asteroids. Two areas of technology research that have been added to the NASA

Charter are ground vehicle propulsion efficiency and energy. NASA does have the program management method and the courage to solve those seemingly impossible engineering problems. However, the down-sizing of the technology work force of NASA, and the over-extension of the employees to work too many programs of critical nature, has diluted the purposes and goals of the NASA's Charter. The work overload and lack of employees stresses the agency and produces confusion and achievement failure neuroses in our government leadership. In addition to all of that political overloading, NASA is expected to excel in all areas of work with no exception. NASA failures cannot be allowed. Probability of failures becomes more likely to reveal catastrophic results when the space agency is under such extraordinary stress.

What does the NASA Charter look like? Section 2472 established the NASA Administrator's position and provides procedures for the Administration functions and limitations.   Section 2473 established the NASA functions and responsibilities of scientific research and development and sharing of that information.

TITLE 42 -
THE PUBLIC HEALTH AND WELFARE
CHAPTER 26 - NATIONAL SPACE PROGRAM

SUBCHAPTER II - COORDINATION OF
AERONAUTICAL AND SPACE ACTIVITIES

SEC. 2473. FUNCTIONS OF ADMINISTRATION
-STATUTE-

(a) Planning, directing, and conducting aeronautical and space activities; participation by scientific community; dissemination of information

The Administration, in order to carry out the purpose of this chapter, shall -

(1) plan, direct, and conduct aeronautical and space activities;

(2) arrange for participation by the scientific community in planning scientific measurements and observations to be made through use of aeronautical and space vehicles, and conduct or arrange for the conduct of such measurements and observations;

(3) provide for the widest practicable and appropriate dissemination of information concerning its activities and the results thereof;

(4) seek and encourage, to the maximum extent possible, the fullest commercial use of space; and

(5) encourage and provide for Federal Government use of commercially provided space services and hardware, consistent with the requirements of the Federal Government.

(b) Research, development, etc., in ground propulsion technologies and solar heating and cooling technologies.

Failure can be embarrassing, even devastating, and NASA deserves a lot of credit for allowing the real truth of the *Challenger* Tragedy to be discovered and reported. NASA was the winner when it came to having reliable and routine access to space. Only the United States had such a vehicle as the Space Shuttle, which was the first real Spaceship. The Soviet Union had a knock-off copy but it only flew once and orbited the Earth for a couple of orbits, unmanned. NASA was truly the world leader of safely launching groups of seven Astronauts into Earth orbit.

This is not to say that NASA looked down upon the Soviet Space Program's accomplishments. That is not the point. The Soviet Union and the citizens had other national and social issues that they were coping with rather than spending money to build a shuttle. The United States government has never underestimated the capabilities and the stamina of the Soviet Space Agency. The Soviets designed and built simple, durable rockets that have kept them on the same page of space exploration history with the United States.

NASA was also a winner in open reporting of the most tragic day in the history of manned spaceflight. NASA was totally accommodating to the concerns and requests of the international army of reporters who covered the Tragedy. It is my hope that NASA will include copies of this book in the libraries of space exploration histories that are located at the space centers.

My recommendation for the complete and total healing for the NASA agency is to get busy with the work of living on Earth, and the work of planning and building space exploration programs of the future. The catalyst to that healing is to educate and recruit the finest engineers, scientists, and technicians, and to employ the vast experience and resources of the people who have developed programs for NASA in the past.

The world needs the ideas and methods that can be provided by the new generations. NASA has shown the world what I call the "**NASA Method**," which formulates how to conduct space exploration most efficiently and with successful results that defy the odds of failure. It is the option of future space explorers to either apply those research and exploration methods, or to ignore those gifts of methodology and procedure that my generation and the generation before mine have given. The "NASA Method" should always include young people and the more experienced elderly people.   Many of the best ideas for space science have not been considered.   I challenge the young people of future generations to study and work in efforts that will add to the bountiful legacy of NASA's exploration and development history.

Two of the NASA engineering managers for the design, development, testing, evaluation, and acceptance of the SRBs were Mr. Lawrence (Larry) Mulloy, SRB Project Manager, and Mr. George Hardy, the Deputy Director of Science and Engineering for SRBs. These two NASA engineers had found the path to ascend the engineering ranks of Marshall Space Flight Center (MSFC) to highly responsible positions in the SRB program.   These men were engineers first, and became managers later in their careers.   Their failures to properly manage the design, development, qualification, and NASA acceptance of the booster system can certainly be forgiven, but should not be forgotten.

If we forget NASA's mistakes in the processing and launching of the 51-L Mission, then we would fail as a society to inform future generations of explorers of the consequences of poor program management.   The managers of the SRB program failed to properly manage the design, development, test qualification, and NASA customer acceptance of the SRBs by hiding the design and performance problems.   It would be a colossal historical mistake to forget that powerful NASA and contractor managers repeatedly opposed the efforts and actions of the KSC SRB engineers and quality control inspectors as the workers detected SRB joint problems during post-flight inspections of the SRB segments.   The crash investigation revealed that several of the KSC engineers and technicians campaigned for a stop of further flights of the substandard performing booster design.   The efforts by those employees to stop the repeated launches of inferior SRBs were concentrated at the SRB retrieval dock on Cape Canaveral Air Force Station, and at NASA KSC engineering.

The period from 1977 until January 28, 1986 presented dozens of indications within NASA and Morton Thiokol that the SRB design was unsafe. There were dysfunctional meetings, unacceptable SRB test results. There were angry emotions between the engineers who made Herculean efforts to get the SRB problems solved versus those who wanted to ignore the reality that the SRB design was not safe. As the months and years passed from 1977 to January 28, 1986, the SRB engineers and managers realized the stupidity and recklessness of the "**Big Lie**" that pretended the SRB design was safe. This situation is evidenced by the MSFC internal memorandum from Mr. Miller to Mr. Eudy, dated January 9, 1978, three years and three months prior to the first Space Shuttle launch, STS-1, *Columbia*, on April 12, 1981. The subject of the memo is *"Restatement of Position on SRM Clevis Joint O-Ring Acceptance Criteria and Clevis Joint Shim Requirements."* The memo pleads with NASA management to support the efforts of engineers to achieve "proper shim size and high quality O-rings that are mandatory to prevent hot gas leaks and resulting catastrophic failure." The *Rogers Presidential Commission Report to the President* included fifteen memos and letters that cried out loudly for the NASA management to redesign the SRB joint structures and seals in order to meet the design and performance specifications for the Space Shuttle SRBs.

It is historic that the NASA management team for the SRB design, development, test, evaluation, and acceptance phases hid the SRB problems from each other, their up-line managers, their down-line engineers, the U.S. Congress, and from the public. The engineers and managers who were defending and running with the "Big Lie" were being chased by NASA and contractor memos, unacceptable test results, and letters in unsuccessful attempts to stop them from running into tragic episodes of Space Shuttle history that would bear their names. As usual, there were faithful public servants sticking their necks out in dutiful efforts to prevent Tragedy and to follow the rules and procedures of the program. Those people should be honored and respected. In the engineering and flight test professions, the meanest and most untrusting act is when facts and issues of design requirements and safety are willfully kept from those people who are responsible for the project or for safe results. Those situations demoralize the trust, respect, and faith of team members for each other. Trust, respect, and faith are necessary for success of a program. Engineering and management malpractice in government programs destroys the public trust and those events will always be remembered by the citizens and by the Press.

Predictable in human behavior, the engineers and managers who were the source of the crushing squeeze of the Boa Constrictor "Big Lie" lured other engineers and managers of government and industry into the "Big Lie." Misery loves company. If a Big Lie exists, but enough people agree that the Big Lie is a true story, then the Big Lie seems justified in the minds of the lie's authors and believers. Humans naturally know from the heart what is right and what is wrong. Even a hardened heart knows the difference, every time.

Larry Mulloy and George Hardy have taken the brunt of the fault in the *Challenger* crash. It must be remembered, however, that the duties and responsibilities of engineers and managers at all levels of the program are—*Do the right thing. Make the right decisions based upon the rules, procedures, and practical sense. Hiding the facts or being afraid of taking an unpopular position in an engineering or management meeting is a lifestyle that helps to build the "Big Lie" for the program.* The program rules and procedures must be followed. Adherence to the rules to get the job done is why the employer pays the salaries. NASA *is* the leader of the American Space Program and no employee of NASA will ever be above the law. The complexities of obeying the law have become more intricate and demanding because international space programs require obedience to not just U.S. laws, but many international and space laws. Space programs have no place for cheaters, employees who are derelict in duty, or employees who think they personally own the government and the taxpayer's money.

There were similar engineering battles being waged in Utah at Morton Thiokol by Roger Boisjoly (pronounced bo-zha-lay) and other excellent engineers employed by Morton Thiokol.

Note that there were excellent NASA employees, like the SRB Systems Section engineers at KSC, who detected, documented, and reported to NASA management the in-flight performance problems of the SRBs. Their engineering and post-flight inspection reports were ignored or waived by NASA management. The SRB lie was huge in its beginnings, and the lie became inflamed and filled with infection. The lie burst and poisoned NASA's reputation forever.

One of my former colleagues, Mr. Paul Schmidt, SRB Section Manager, led a lonely struggle to convince NASA management that the SRB performance was not safe and that further flights must be stopped until the SRB joint design problems could be solved. Paul is a good man and so are the NASA and contractor employees who worked for him. Paul and his team of engineers, quality inspectors, and technicians became familiar with the routine of discovering and docu-

menting SRB primary O-ring hot gas blow-by detected
during the post-flight disassembly of the SRB segments.
The team wrote up the defects and performance degra-
dations on NASA forms called Problem Reports (PRs)
that were consistently waived, overruled, or ignored by
NASA management.

Paul knew the reality and consequences of the
infectious lie that NASA management had on their
tongues regarding the SRB O-ring malfunctions and hot
gas blow-bys. Paul and his team had repeatedly tried
to expose it and heal the infection, but a couple of felonious NASA managers wagged their tongues well to
promote the deceit until the boil on their tongues burst.
The SRB lie infection ultimately killed seven Astronauts,
destroyed a great workhorse spaceship, *Challenger*,
horrified millions of people, and severely damaged the
reputations of a great exploration industry.

Former President of the United States, William
Howard Taft, spoke at Georgia Institute of Technology
in Atlanta, Georgia on May 11, 1911. As reported by
Georgia Tech's Alumni Magazine, President Taft was
wise enough to realize the value and worth of properly
conducted engineering work. Recall that President Taft
gave this speech during a dynamic period of post-
American Civil War recovery and rebuilding. That year
of 1911 was when the industrial revolution was running
"full steam." It had been just over seven years since the
first successful airplane flight of 1903 by Wilbur and
Orville Wright.

President Taft said, *"I consider the honest engineer the
most valuable asset of this government. These are the reasons why.
Dishonesty in any other branch of the service can be overcome in some
way. In some way we can recover from it; in some way we can rally
from it, but dishonesty on the part of the engineer is always so far
reaching in the loss of property, money, of time, of human lives, that
dishonesty on the part of the engineer is irreparable."*

CHAPTER 13

NEVER THOUGHT
I'D BE DOING THIS

I worked for NASA because that agency had the environment through which I could express myself with my contributions to other people. I worked for NASA because of the agency's history of teamwork, sharing, and excellence. How did I feel about the unplanned work period of the *Challenger* Tragedy investigation? I never thought I'd be doing this. The bizarre nature of everything that transpired during the investigation made the experience of the investigation seem overwhelming. The grief and horror of losing the Astronauts, and losing the mission to which they were committed, made the situation even more tragic. The 51-L mission was the job of the Astronauts, and they all loved their jobs, even with all the politics, technical setbacks, the obvious risks, and the blatant dangers. A very important lesson that the 51-L Astronauts certainly would have liked for all of us to accept is the lesson of commitment to honorable work. We must make our work places proper and functional, with an atmosphere conducive to achieving a quality product, and guidelines that are mandatory to follow by management and employees. If we plan for the mission together, even if we "fail," we will be able to cope with the outcome. Our work efforts should be for each other, not just for ourselves. The lessons contained in this drama of life as taught by NASA and the *Challenger* crew are many. Dick Scobee, the *Challenger* Commander, usually encouraged and assisted the "underdogs" who were of good intentions and goals but who had no support or sponsors. His U.S. Air Force experiences taught Scobes what it was like to experience the challenging uphill climb to achieve one's goals when a person has to start at the bottom of the organization.

If program leaders selfishly circumvent the ethical and moral paths of work practices and guide- lines, workers may find themselves in assignments similar to my investigation assignment of 1986. I liter- ally had to sift through the *Challenger* wreckage. I was shocked when, during the inspection of the Crew Module wreckage, we found an object that we thought was part of the Orbiter, but was in fact a molar tooth from one of the Astronauts. That event was bleak and depressing. I found Asian, African-American, and Caucasian hair in the most unimaginable locations of the debris. Other investigators had similar experiences.

The nasty job of handling the debris was horri- fying at times. I was analyzing part of the primary structural beams and pressure vessel of the aft pressure bulkhead of the Crew Module when I discovered more human remains. It was painful to imagine the momentum that was necessary to have caused such destruction. These men and women had been my colleagues and the graphic evidence of their deaths was agonizing.

Picking up the remains of my colleagues, handling the shattered pieces of a great performing spaceship, and realizing the losses to our flying customers, the payloads industry, combined to deliver enough sadness to last a lifetime. I prayed that the lives and experiences of the deceased Astronauts would be examples to many people for how to live better lives.

In 1973, I was a senior in high school and was all set to go to the Naval Academy and then on to flight school to train for piloting the new F-14 Tomcat fighter jet with the U.S. Navy, or perhaps the new Harrier Jump-jet with the U.S. Marines.   My plan was to accumulate 1,500 hours of multi-engine jet time and then apply to NASA to become a Space Shuttle pilot. The surplus of military pilots after the Vietnam War and my near-sighted myopic eyes sent me on a different journey to the Georgia Tech College of Aerospace Engineering and on to NASA.   Had my eyesight been 20/20 when I graduated from high school, it would have been chronologically possible that I could have been Dick Scobee's pilot for the 51-L Mission.

The year 1973, plus four years at the Naval Academy, plus four years of active duty and flight time, was timely for me to have been Commander Dick Scobee's rookie pilot for the 51-L Mission, instead of Mike Smith.   I could have been a NASA Astronaut for five years by 1986.   I thought about this many times during the crash investigation.   The Astronaut remains in the wreckage could have been mine.   Perhaps you understand more clearly now why I had to share the truth about *Challenger*.   That left seat in the Space Shuttle Crew Module was one of my goals for my life; the crash investigation activities that I performed regarding that right front seat of *Challenger* were heartbreaking.

Whatever your family is like, whatever your job is like, and whatever your spiritual and social views may be, failure and death is a common denominator for us all.   The choices we make with our families and our actions as we work our jobs are critical because other people are relying upon us to make the right decisions and follow the best rules.   The *Challenger* crew and the NASA and contractor employees understood this reality very well.

CHAPTER 14

THE SPARROWS OF *Challenger*

Originally, the title of this book was "The Sparrows of *Challenger*." The change of the title to "The Truth About *Challenger*" was from an experience that I had in 1990 when I was traveling to California to support a Space Shuttle landing. An eleven year-old boy was sitting near me at the Orlando airport while we waited for our airplane flight to California. We were watching the *Cable News Network (CNN)* replay of a Space Shuttle launch that had occurred the day before. The boy's comments indicated that he was very interested in the Space Shuttle launch. I mentioned to the boy that I had worked to launch that Space Shuttle. The boy said, "I'd like to fly on a Shuttle, but not like the one that blew up." I said, "You must have been about six years old when the *Challenger* crashed." He said, "Yep, about that old." I asked him, "If there were a book about the *Challenger* crash that would tell you the story of what happened, what would you call that book?" With immediate response the boy said, "The Truth About *Challenger*." The curious and innocent perspective of that boy convinced me that his sugges-tion was the proper title. His imagination inspired me in a way that made me believe that his generation will want to know "The Truth About *Challenger*."

After the *Challenger* Tragedy happened in the winter of 1986 and the grueling details of the investi-gation continued into the spring months, an amazing thing occurred at the site where the Crew Module wreckage was located. Each day, sparrows flew around the wreckage and under the carport structure above the Crew Module pieces. One day, I noticed that the sparrows had built a nest on one of the white, aluminum I-beams of the rear pressure bulkhead of the Crew Module. The nest was made of grass that was like straw, small sticks, and wreckage. It was very well made and the sparrows selected a beam that was located up about half the height of the vertically positioned bulkhead.

I climbed up onto a ladder and peered onto the I-beam to see if there were any sparrow eggs in the nest. There were two. For the moment, I totally forgot that I was standing amongst the ashes and debris of the American Space Program. The hope for new life and the site of the living going about the natural order of life was refreshing and uplifting.

I told the other investigators about the sparrow bird nest so that we could share this event. We investigators had been through hell for months; those little birds gave us some relief and hope as we marveled at their skills of living. After a couple of days with the freshly laid sparrow eggs, the excitement of the birds waned and the familiar work routine continued. One afternoon, Ron Phelps, the site manager, told me to remove the nest. I was disappointed that anyone would think of disturbing the family of sparrows, much less destroying their nest that required skill, determination, and commitment to construct. Those work qualities of the sparrows are the same qualities of those of us who designed, built, and flew the Space Shuttle.

There we were, on a National Wildlife Refuge, in the midst of the remains of a three billion dollar Orbiter that had been destroyed while flying, and I was being ordered to remove the nest of innocent sparrows. No way! Those sparrows had no concept of property lines. Their only interest in *Challenger* was to build a nest on the piece of structure that seemed to provide their young with safety and security to ensure better odds for their survival.

The Human Race had already given up on the wreckage of *Challenger* as having any appreciable value. Except for the secrets of the Space Shuttle breakup sequence, the wreckage was only worth so much per pound to scrap dealers. The sparrows viewed that scrap aluminum bulkhead as the perfect home foundation. I am positive that *Challenger's* Commander, Dick Scobee, would have appreciated those sparrows and their attempt to have family and to survive with the rest of the world.

I have a certain dedication and loyalty, but I was not going to allow the nest to be removed. I told Kelly Longhofer that under no circumstances would he be authorized to remove that nest. I had limited authority over Kelly, but Kelly is a good man and he wanted the nest and sparrow family to stay anyway. We managed to make Ron forget about removing the nest.

One day, the sparrow chicks hatched from their eggs. The chicks soon began chirping. I felt like a father because I was so proud of the baby chicks. They and their parents were allowed into the debris area even without a NASA clearance. After all, the sparrow's ancestors belonged in the restricted area first, thousands of years ago.

The chicks grew, became strong, and began to realize that there was much more to the world than their comfortable nest with a roof over their beaks. The *Challenger* family— the birds and the investigators— all got along well. The sparrows and investigators were going about our responsibilities, living amongst the broken pieces of what was one of the most phenomenal and historic flying machines of the world.

As great as the *Challenger* had been as a flying machine, she represented merely an attempt to copy the perfect design of the sparrows.

Years have passed since the *Challenger* Tragedy and the birth of those sparrow chicks. Somewhere in that Merritt Island National Wildlife Refuge, the descendants of those *Challenger* 51-L sparrows are starting the process of living all over again. Their skills of living, playing, building, and preparing to introduce the future to the newborns are remarkably similar to the character and actions of rocket engineers and Astronauts with whom I have worked.

Life is filled with hazards and the chance of people dying by accident increases as we take the risks. The sparrow nest was constructed high above the ground. Every component of the sparrow's nest was gathered at some risk, but the completed nest supported and protected life. The sparrows took the risks of living around humans and other predators for the opportunity to secure a future from snakes that are more hazardous to sparrows than are humans.

The *Challenger* sparrow family of 1986 was able to fly away from the destroyed Crew Module. For them, the *Challenger* was a safe place to live. I think of the sparrows of *Challenger* as a reminder that people have the right to live and come to understand as much about the Universe as they can in a lifetime.

CHAPTER 15

THE BURIAL OF *Challenger*

One day, late in the *Challenger* investigation, Ken Colley instructed me to go to the Cape Canaveral Air Force Station and evaluate two abandoned underground missile silos that had been the launch Pads for the *Minuteman* nuclear missile system deployment. My task was to take measurements of the inside of the silos. This seemed like a strange assignment, but what in our lives had not been strange for the past six months? I asked Ken many questions in my efforts to understand what I was to measure and why. I was instructed to inspect the silos for their configuration, dimensions, and general condition.

My friend and colleague, Henry Crunk, was a NASA engineer who worked vehicle handling and access engineering in our section. Henry looked exactly like Catholic Pope John Paul. Everywhere we traveled with him, many Catholics who saw us thought that Henry was the Pope and that I was a bodyguard for the Pope. Henry was a very polite, southern, Christian man born in Huntsville, Alabama who began his NASA career working with the legendary Dr. Wernher von Braun of NASA.

Henry was assigned to be the team leader for the inspection of the missile silos. He was always good at encouraging a team along as he watched them do the work. Henry was great supervisory material. A newly hired engineer from our office was also assigned to the silo inspection team.

I was unsure exactly why the silos needed inspecting and measuring, so I asked why we were required to do this task. Ken said, "Crippen (Astronaut and Crash Investigation Boss) has made the decision to bury the *Challenger* debris inside the two underground silos."

Burial? The thought never occurred to me. The majority of the investigation was over, and redesign of the SRBs was already underway. Ron Phelps called a meeting that day to instruct the investigation team at the Logistics Facility that our next objective would be to prepare the wooden crates of *Challenger* debris to be shipped to the *Minuteman* missile silos at the Cape. The very large pieces would be buried along with the boxed pieces.

My first thought was that all of the unique pieces of the destroyed Space Shuttle would be taken away, and that the plans to use selected *Challenger* pieces for engineering models were canceled. At the time, the decision to bury *Challenger* in the silos seemed wasteful. Looking back today, I think that Bob Crippen made the right decision. The landing gear from the left wing of the Orbiter was one of a few *Challenger* pieces salvaged. The landing gear was used at NASA Langley in the outdoor, high-speed, water-powered sled to conduct landing gear, wheel, and brake testing.

I drove the three of us engineers in a gray government van from KSC for the fifteen-mile drive to the Cape where the 1960s vintage *Minuteman* silos were located. We were told that someone would be at the perimeter gate of the silos and they would allow us entry.

We approached the silo complex along the famous "Cape Row" of launch Pads. We saw a U.S. Air Force airman in the center of the road, dressed in camouflaged fatigues, with an M-16 rifle slung onto her shoulder. Henry and I just looked at each other and realized that there was more to this data-gathering trip to the silos than we were told.

The airman stopped us and said, "We've been expecting you. Continue straight ahead and stop at the checkpoint gate." Now we were really wondering what was going on. There was another airman guarding the main gate to the silo complex. After checking our clearances, the second airman passed us through the gate so we could drive to the silos.

I parked the van adjacent to one of the two silo dome caps. The dome cap was a fiberglass, wood, and concrete structure positioned at ground level. From ground level, there were about ten concrete steps that descended below to a door that led into the silo. We walked down the several steps to the metal door of the silo. Then we opened the door and peered into the very dark, damp, and drafty stairwell that continued the descent into the silo—and whatever was inside the silo. This was somewhat spooky.

We realized that we needed to get a flashlight. We decided to go back to the office for all the proper equipment since by then we understood what we were sent to inspect. We climbed the stairs back to the ground level and walked to the van. As we walked on the grass, I looked around within the fenced complex of the silos. I noticed that the bushes and trees were waving like waves on the ocean. I focused on this strange sight and realized that I was looking at military camouflage, acres of it.

I said to Henry, "We are surrounded by camouflage nets. Look." Henry said, "Where?" I said, "Everywhere, Henry. Look." Henry finally recognized it. We were wondering what was going on out there at that dilapidated and condemned launch site.

Another airman with an M-16 rifle walked

nearby. I told Henry that I would ask the airman for some flashlights. Henry thought that we should not bother with the airmen any more than we needed. I asked the other airman for assistance. He was very accommodating and offered to get us several flashlights. He said, "Follow me." We went around a corner of the camouflage netting and I was very surprised to walk right into a small city of airmen, loads of sophisticated electronic equipment, and satellite dish antennae. A group of airmen were playing volleyball, of all things.

I asked the airman what this beachside gathering was about. He told me that they were American airmen stationed in Europe, and they were participating in a global communications exercise in which they were given surprise notice and dispatched to Cape Canaveral, Florida within a few hours to support the operation.

I got the flashlights and returned to the entrance of the silo and entered the abyss. Henry was nervous about entering a silo that could be full of snakes. He pushed on my back as I descended the stairwell, and said, "Go ahead, Randy, you're doing good, I'm right behind you." I said, "I'm sure you are Henry, but I think you should go first, you're the team leader." He responded, "That's right. I am the leader and I say you go first."

I was cautiously taking steps while following the flashlight beam, while looking for snakes, spiders, rats, armadillos, raccoons, alligators, and anything else that may want to bite, sting, or eat us. The steps descended deeply underground and led to a landing where there was an equipment room about 20 ft. x 20 ft. square. It was pitch black dark in that room until I shined the flashlight into the dungeon.   It was flooded with murky water about one foot deep. There were over-head aluminum cable trays for electrical wiring. Rusted and dangling from the ceiling were the antique ceiling lights from the 1960s. There was a straight-back, armless government chair sitting in the center of the room in the foot-deep water. The sight of that chair gave me the sense that a person who used to work in that room had just recently left the room, even though the silos had been unoccupied for years.

I panned the beam of light from left to right as all three of us engineers peered into the equipment room, observing everything we could. The beam of light illuminated a bank of severely corroded acid backup batteries. There was a gooey crud oozing from the casings of the batteries and pooling at the base into the murky water. That room was intimidating and we had only just begun our descent into the silo.

Pressing onward, I led the way down and down, further into the cool, drafty, sub-terranian cavern. As we descended the steps, we arrived at an opening to the main silo. We cautiously looked into the silo, expecting to see a deep concrete hole with water at the bottom. Instead, we could see only a few feet onto a circular, aluminum access platform that had been hoisted into position by winches on vertical tracks. The platform operated years ago to provide access for maintenance to the *Minuteman* rocket. The platform was positioned and secured at the top of the silo to reduce the distance that people or animals would fall if they were to fall through the fiberglass dome at the top center of the silo. The access platform was littered with trash.

We continued to descend the stairs to the bottom and noticed that the base of the silo was clut-tered with all sorts of debris: lunch wrappers, drink containers, pencils, paper, and miscellaneous pieces of junk that over the years had been tossed into the silo from workers at the abandoned missile site.   The garbage in the silo was a collection of product marketing and advertising from the previous twenty years.

There is something unique about being at the bottom of a dark, cold, and drafty hole in the Earth. There is a distorted sense of hope as one looks up from the bottom of the silo to the sunlight sneaking into the door edge of the fiberglass dome.   One thing was for sure–I was not going to get too close to the critters living amongst the trash pile at the bottom of the silo. I was content to meet the vast Florida wildlife on the ground level, not in a pit, thank you.

We recorded the measurements of the silo and ascended the many steps to the ground level, only to stop and shine the flashlight into the eerie equipment room again.   We decided to report the leaking batteries as hazardous waste for a cleanup later.   When we exited the silo, we felt as if we had arrived from another life.   We got into the van and left that place, thanking the military personnel as we passed them. We drove back to KSC from the Cape and went inside Complex-A where our main office was located.   We met with my Branch Manager, Ken Colley, who sent us on this epic voyage into the great abyss.   Ken asked, "What took you guys so long?"   We attempted to tell him this story, but he didn't understand the details without actually having been inside the silos.

Two silos were required to entomb the large volume of *Challenger* wreckage.   I never thought that I would be measuring the grave for one of the finest spaceships in history.   Boxes of debris and large, loose pieces of the grand old NASA workhorse, *Challenger*, were buried and sealed with giant concrete slabs. The next person in the future who may enter the silo grave will need much more equipment than just a few flashlights.

I invested a staggering amount of time in 1986 as a crash investigator of a team that contributed findings, observations, data, and scientific summaries for the Space Shuttle Breakup Analysis to the *Presidential Report on the Challenger Accident*. In the 1990s, I spent many hours at the Georgia Tech library, researching information contained within the Presidential Report on the *Challenger* Accident to be used in the writing of this book. I now want to show that smaller portions of the report are available on the Internet. This information can be accessed by searching for "Presidential Commission Report on Space Shuttle *Challenger* Accident" at the website, www.KSC.nasa.gov.

Report of the Presidential Commission On the Space Shuttle Challenger Accident

(In compliance with Executive Order 12546 of February 3, 1986)
TABLE OF CONTENTS

VOLUME I

VOLUME II

VOLUME III

Appendix N - NASA Photo and television Support Team
Report
Appendix O - NASA Search, Recovery and Reconstruction
Task Force Team Report

VOLUME IV

Hearings of the Presidential Commission on the Space Shuttle
Challenger Accident: February 6, 1986 to February 25, 1986

VOLUME V

Hearings of the Presidential Commission on the Space Shuttle
Challenger Accident: February 26, 1986 to May 2, 1986.

The following information is a portion of *The
Rogers Presidential Commission Report on The Space Shuttle
Challenger Accident*, dated June 6, 1986. This is a brief
look at the cause of the accident, findings, and the
Commission's conclusion. The five-volume report
contains a much greater volume of information about
the Space Shuttle and the 51-L crash investigation.

As you will hopefully detect as you read, the
Presidential Commission's Report concludes, *"The specific
failure was the destruction of the seals that are intended to prevent hot
gases from leaking through the joint during the propellant burn of the
rocket motor."* I have never agreed with this aspect of the
Commission's Report that the *failure*, or *specific failure*,
was the O-ring seals. I have always maintained that the
failure was the inadequate stiffness in the structural
design of the SRB steel casing. I have also maintained
that the O-ring damage from hot gas blow-by was the
malfunction that was initiated by the ***failure*** when
the steel joint rotated or flexed at ignition of the SRBs.
This semantic flaw of the report is significant when
analyzing a spacecraft for failure modes and malfunctions.

VOLUME I, CHAPTER IV

THE CAUSE OF THE ACCIDENT

The consensus of the Commission and participating investigative agencies is that the loss of the Space Shuttle Challenger was caused by a failure in the joint between the two lower segments of the right Solid Rocket Motor. <u>The specific failure was the destruction of the seals</u> that are intended to prevent hot gases from leaking through the joint during the propellant burn of the rocket motor. <u>The evidence assembled by the Commission indicates that no other element of the Space Shuttle system contributed to this failure.</u>

In arriving at this conclusion, the Commission reviewed in detail all available data, reports and records, directed and supervised numerous tests, analysis, and experiments by NASA, civilian contractors and various government agencies, and then developed specific scenarios and the range of most probable causative factors.

FINDINGS

1. A combustion gas leak through the right Solid Rocket Motor aft field joint initiated at or shortly after ignition eventually weakened and/or penetrated the External Tank, initiating vehicle structural breakup and loss of the Space Shuttle Challenger during STS Mission 51-L.

2. The evidence shows that no other STS 51-L Shuttle element or the payload contributed to the causes of the right Solid Rocket Motor aft field joint combustion gas leakage. Sabotage was not a factor.

3.   Evidence examined in the review of Space Shuttle material, manufacturing, assembly, quality control, and processing on non-conformance reports found no flight hardware shipped to the launch site that fell outside the limits of Shuttle design specifications.

4. *Launch site activities, including assembly and preparation, from receipt of the flight hardware to launch were generally in accord with established procedures and were not considered a factor in the accident.*

5. *Launch site records show that the right Solid Rocket Motor segments were assembled using approved procedures. However, significant out-of-round conditions existed between the two segments joined at the right Solid Rocket Motor aft field joint (the joint that failed).*

> *a. While the assembly conditions had the potential of generating debris or damage that could cause O-ring seal failure, these were not considered factors in this accident.*

> *b. The diameters of the two Solid Rocket Motor segments had grown as a result of prior use.*

> *c. The growth resulted in a condition at time of launch wherein the maximum gap between the tang and clevis in the region of the joint's O-rings was no more than .008 inches and the average gap would have been .004 inches.*

> *d. With a tang-to-clevis gap of .004 inches, the O-ring in the joint would be compressed to the extent that it pressed against all three walls of the O-ring retaining channel.*

> *e. The lack of roundness of the segments was such that the smallest tang-to-clevis clearance occurred at the initiation of the assembly operation at positions of 120 degrees and 300 degrees around the circumference of the aft field joint. It is uncertain if this tight condition and the resultant greater compression of the O-rings at these points persisted to the time of launch.*

6. *The ambient temperature at time of launch was 36°F., or 15° lower than the next coldest previous launch.*

a. The temperature at the 300-degree position on the right aft field joint circumference was estimated to be 28° plus or minus 5°F. This was the coldest point on the joint.

b. Temperature on the opposite side of the right Solid Rocket Booster facing the sun was estimated to be about 50°F.

7. *Other joints on the left and right Solid Rocket Boosters experienced similar combinations of tang-to-clevis gap clearance and temperature. It is not known whether these joints experienced distress during the flight of 51-L.*

8. *Experimental evidence indicates that due to several effects associated with the Solid Rocket Booster's ignition and combustion pressures and associated vehicle motions, the gap between the tang and the clevis will open as much as .017 and .029 inches at the secondary and primary O-rings, respectively.*

a. This opening begins upon ignition, reaches its maximum rate of opening at about 200-300 milliseconds, and is essentially complete at 600 milliseconds when the Solid Rocket Booster reaches its operating pressure.

b. The External Tank and right Solid Rocket Booster are connected by several struts, including one at 310 degrees near the aft field joint that failed. This strut's effect on the joint dynamics is to enhance the opening of the gap between the tang and clevis by about 10-20 percent in the region of 300-320 degrees.

9. *O-ring resiliency is directly related to its temperature.*

a. A warm O-ring that has been compressed will return to its original shape much quicker than will a cold O-ring when compression is relieved. Thus, a warm O-ring will follow the opening of the tang-to-clevis gap. A cold O-ring may not.

b. A compressed O-ring at 75°F. is five times more responsive in returning to its uncompressed shape than a cold O-ring at 30°F.

c. As a result, it is probable that the O-rings in the right solid booster aft field joint were not following the opening of the gap between the tang and clevis at time of ignition.

10. Experiments indicate that the primary mechanism that actuates O-ring sealing is the application of gas pressure to the upstream (high-pressure) side of the O-ring as it sits in its groove or channel.

a. For this pressure actuation to work most effectively, a space between the O-ring and its upstream channel wall should exist during pressurization.

b. A tang-to-clevis gap of .004 inches, as probably existed in the failed joint, would have initially compressed the O-ring to the degree that no clearance existed between the O-ring and its upstream channel wall and the other two surfaces of the channel.

c. At the cold launch temperature experienced, the O-ring would be very slow in returning to its normal rounded shape. It would not follow the opening of the tang-to-clevis gap. It would remain in its compressed position in the O-ring channel and not provide a space between itself and the upstream channel wall. Thus, it is probable the O-ring would not be pressure actuated to seal the gap in time to preclude joint failure due to blow-by and erosion from hot combustion gases.

11. The sealing characteristics of the Solid Rocket Booster O-rings are enhanced by timely application of motor pressure.

a. Ideally, motor pressure should be applied to actuate the O-ring and seal the joint prior to significant opening of the tang-to-clevis gap (100 to 200 milliseconds after motor ignition).

b. Experimental evidence indicates that temperature, humidity and other variables in the putty compound used to seal the joint can delay pressure application to the joint by 500 milliseconds or more.

c. This delay in pressure could be a factor in initial joint failure.

12.   *Of 21 launches with ambient temperatures of 61°F. or greater, only four showed signs of O-ring thermal distress; i.e., erosion or blow-by and soot. Each of the launches below 61°F. resulted in one or more O-rings showing signs of thermal distress.*

a. Of these improper joint sealing actions, one-half occurred in the aft field joints, 20 percent in the center field joints, and 30 percent in the upper field joints. The division between left and right Solid Rocket Boosters was roughly equal.

b. Each instance of thermal O-ring distress was accompanied by a leak path in the insulating putty. The leak path connects the rocket's combustion chamber with the O-ring region of the tang and clevis. Joints that actuated without incident may also have had these leak paths.

13.   *There is a possibility that there was water in the clevis of the STS 51-L joints, since water was found in the STS-9 joints during a de-stack operation after exposure to less rainfall than STS 51-L. At time of launch, it was cold enough that water present in the joint would freeze. Tests show that ice in the joint can inhibit proper secondary seal performance.*

14.   A series of puffs of smoke were observed emanating from the 51-L aft field joint area of the right Solid Rocket Booster between 0.678 and 2.500 seconds after ignition of the Shuttle Solid Rocket Motors.

a. The puffs appeared at a frequency of about three puffs per second. This roughly matches the natural structural frequency of the solids at lift off and is reflected in slight cyclic changes of the tang-to-clevis gap opening.

b. The puffs were seen to be moving upward along the surface of the booster above the aft field joint.

c. The smoke was estimated to originate at a circumferential position of between 270 degrees and 315 degrees on the booster aft field joint, emerging from the top of the joint.

15.   This smoke from the aft field joint at Shuttle lift off was the first sign of the failure of the Solid Rocket Booster O-ring seals on STS 51-L.

16.   The leak was again clearly evident as a flame at approximately 58 seconds into the flight. It is possible that the leak was continuous but unobservable or non-existent in portions of the intervening period. It is possible in either case that thrust vectoring and normal vehicle response to wind shear as well as planned maneuvers reinitiated or magnified the leakage from a degraded seal in the period preceding the observed flames. The estimated position of the flame, centered at a point 307 degrees around the circumference of the aft field joint, was confirmed by the recovery of two fragments of the right Solid Rocket Booster.

a. A small leak could have been present that may have grown to breach the joint in flame at a time on the order of 58 to 60 seconds after lift off.

b. Alternatively, the O-ring gap could have been resealed by deposition of a fragile buildup of aluminum oxide and other combustion debris. This resealed section of the joint could have been disturbed by thrust vectoring, Space Shuttle motion and flight loads inducted by changing winds aloft.

c. The winds aloft caused control actions in the time interval of 32 seconds to 62 seconds into the flight that were typical of the largest values experienced on previous missions.

Most organizations in aviation talk about safety in one form or another in hopes that by discussing it, somehow the hazards, risks, and exposures in life are reduced to a survivable level. Organizations like NASA are never infallible, although the ambition is to strive for perfection, despite the fact that opinions often differ as to what constitutes perfection.

The Presidential Report on the *Challenger* Accident addressed the realities of how the NASA Solid Rocket Booster Program began and was allowed by NASA management to continue to operate with a substandard and unaccountable safety program for such technology applications. Volume I, Chapter VI of the Presidential Report captures what we investigators discovered in 1986 during the investigation regarding how the SRBs were allowed to fly with such critical design, performance, and safety problems. The absence of experienced safety personnel and safety activities during Shuttle processing was obvious to the investigators. The repeated NASA cover-ups of malfunctioning SRB O-rings from previous flights culminated in NASA dispositions of those post-flight inspection results as "approved for unrestricted flight."

The Commission realized that the crash could have occurred on any of the previous 24 Shuttle flights. NASA had a safety and quality system in place, but management failed to properly apply and manage that system and its people. It was also obvious that NASA management had lost the desire to allow safety, quality, and reliability to lead the way for Space Shuttle activities. Concern developed regarding the decline in safety practices since the first launch of the Space Shuttle, STS-1, April 12, 1981.

VOLUME I, CHAPTER VII
THE SILENT SAFETY PROGRAM

The Commission was surprised to realize after many hours of testimony that NASA's safety staff was never mentioned. No witness related the approval or disapproval of the reliability engineers, and none expressed the satisfaction or dissatisfaction of the quality assurance staff. No one thought to invite a safety representative or a reliability and quality assurance engineer to the January 27, 1986, teleconference between Marshall and Thiokol. Similarly, there was no representative of safety on the Mission Management Team that made key decisions during the countdown on January 28, 1986. The Commission is concerned about the symptoms that it sees.

The unrelenting pressure to meet the demands of an accelerating flight schedule might have been adequately handled by NASA if it had insisted upon the exactingly thorough procedures that were its hallmark during the Apollo Program. An extensive and redundant safety program comprising interdependent safety, reliability, and quality assurance functions existed during and after the lunar program to discover any potential safety problems. Between that period and 1986, however, the program became ineffective. This loss of effectiveness seriously degraded the checks and balances essential for maintaining flight safety.

On April 3, 1986, Arnold Aldrich, the Space Shuttle Program manager, appeared before the Commission at a public hearing in Washington, DC He described five different communication or organization failures that affected the launch decision on January 28, 1986. Four of those failures relate directly to faults within the safety program. These faults include a lack of problem reporting requirements, inadequate trend analysis, and misrepresentation of criticality and lack of involvement in critical discussions. A properly staffed, supported, and robust safety organization might well have avoided these faults and thus eliminated the communication failures.

NASA has a safety program to ensure that the communication failures to which Mr. Aldrich referred do not occur. In the case of mission 51-L, that program fell short.

FINDINGS

1. Reductions in the safety, reliability and quality assurance work force at Marshall and NASA Headquarters have seriously limited capability in those vital functions.

2. Organizational structures at Kennedy and Marshall have placed safety, reliability, and quality assurance offices under the supervision of the very organizations and activities whose efforts they are to check.

3. Problem reporting requirements are not concise and fail to get critical information to the proper levels of management.

4. Little or no trend analysis was performed on O-ring erosion and blow-by problems.

5. As the flight rate increased, the Marshall safety, reliability and quality assurance work force was decreasing, which adversely affected mission safety.

6. Five weeks after the 51-L accident, the criticality of the Solid Rocket Motor field joint was still not properly documented in the problem reporting system at Marshall.

(Source: The Presidential Commission on the Space Shuttle Challenger Accident Report, June 6, 1986 p.152, p161)

Additional specific information for clarification of the catastrophic failure modes of the vehicle from the Challenger Accident Report

"...the fact that all material failures occurred from overload with no evidence of internal burn damage or exposure to explosive forces indicates that destruction of the Orbiter occurred predominantly from aerodynamic, acceleration, and inertial forces that exceeded design limits."

"The structural evaluation established clearly that the Crew Module, including most of the outer shell, remained essentially intact until impact with water <u>and that the Crew Module was fragmented excessively from extreme overload and inertial forces associated with water impact</u>. The structural deformations and fragmentations indicate that the module struck the water in a slight nose down and steep left bank attitude."

(Source: The Presidential Commission on the Space Shuttle Challenger Accident Report, June 6, 1986, Vol. III, p. O-23, Section F, Item 2)

CONCLUSION

In view of the findings, <u>the Commission concluded that the cause of the Challenger accident was the failure of the pressure seal in the aft field joint of the right Solid Rocket Booster</u>. The failure was due to a faulty design unacceptably sensitive to a number of factors. These factors were the effects of temperature, physical dimensions, the character of materials, the effects of reusability, processing and the reaction of the joint to dynamic loading.

(Source: The Presidential Commission on the Space Shuttle Challenger Accident Report, June 6, 1986 p.40, p.70-81)

It is now time to learn the Truth - *the exact cause* - of the *Challenger* crash. The *Rogers Presidential Commission Report* focused upon the little O-ring of the Solid Rocket Booster's field joint as the *failure* that caused the crash of the *Challenger.* Wasn't the failure actually whatever caused the blow-by of hot gases past primary and secondary O-rings? Or did the O-ring simply *malfunction?* What, then, was the primary *failure* of the Space Shuttle *Challenger* components during the flight? Let me explain.

Media reports and statements in the *Report of the Presidential Commission on the Space Shuttle <u>Challenger</u> Accident* about the crash and investigation have promoted the O-rings as the *failure* that led to the crash of the *Challenger,*

BUT THE SRB FIELD JOINT O-RINGS <u>WERE NOT THE FAILURE.</u>

The O-rings were <u>victims</u> of the actual failure. The eventual redesign of the actual failure reportedly cost the American taxpayers several hundred million dollars, according to the briefings given to the NASA engineers during 1988. If the O-rings had been the failure, then why did NASA retain the two original O-rings and add a third O-ring that is like the original two O-rings? Furthermore, O-rings do not cost several hundred million dollars.

Which part of the Space Shuttle was redesigned to eliminate the failure mode of the Space Shuttle SRBs? In actuality, *the redesigned parts are portions of the steel structural casings of the SRB joints.* The ends of the cylinder-shaped SRB casings, or segments, were redesigned and machined to new geometry and dimensions. *The structural stiffness of the original SRB joints was not stiff enough to control the performance of the O-rings.*   That extra flexibility of the original SRB joints allowed the joints to "rotate" or kick out in a binding configuration that resulted in the O-ring being lifted from the sealing surface of the joint-to-O-ring interface.   The original O-rings were essentially just along for the ride.

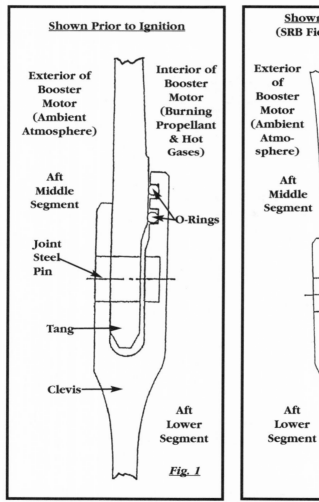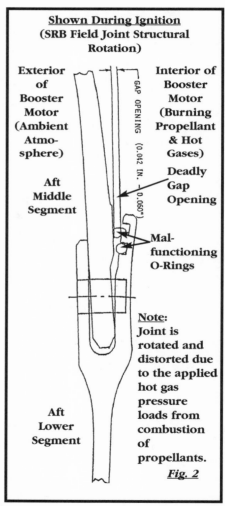

Space Shuttle Solid Rocket Booster Motor Segment Joint Design
(See explanations of *Fig. 1* and *Fig. 2* on page 177.)

Fig1--This is a sketch of the SRB joint design that was flown on STS-1 through STS-25 (Mission 51-L, *Challenger*). There are four motor segments that stack vertically to form one SRB. The SRB has three major "Field Joints" where the four segments attach to each other. It was the lower aft field joint of the right SRB that failed in flight on *Challenger* Mission 51-L. This sketch shows the SRB joint assembly being geometrically distorted from hundreds of pounds of pressure per square inch inside the SRB. The extra long tang allowed for too much flexure of the tang and clevis joint rendering the O-rings malfunctional. The SRB joint failure was that the SRB joints were not structurally stiff enough. The O-ring mal-function was that the O-rings could not reliably perform their intended function of sealing the asbestos putty in place.

In 1977, NASA, Marshall Space Flight Center, had determined that this design would not function safely and reliably due to the phenomenon called **"Joint Rotation"** in which the segment joints would flex or rotate at as shown and lift the O-rings from the sealing surface metal thus allowing the 800 psi pressure inside the SRB motor to force the Asbestos Putty **("Lucky Putty")** from the joint. Joint Rotation occurs at ignition of the SRB on the launch Pad, and can continue to cycle during flight. The hot gases then contact the rubber O-rings producing erosion and melting. The hot gases exceed the thermal capability of the steel casing of the SRB motor and the SRB casing melts, resulting in a leak in the SRB casing and destruction of the SRB and Space Shuttle.

Several engineers at NASA and Morton Thiokol made several heroic efforts to change the SRB field joint design that was destined for Tragedy, but the management chose not to follow the professional advice and pleadings of their engineers. This deliberate failure of management to follow the NASA rules and procedures shows how even if a great system of accountability is in place, it can fail if humans deliberately choose not to follow the rules and procedures.

Fig. 2--This exaggerated sketch shows how the SRB field joint (with the weak and flexible clevis and tang structural design) will momentarily 'rotate" and lift the O-rings up off of their sealing surfaces rendering the O-rings mal-functional and resulting in the catastrophic loss of the Space Shuttle, the Astronauts, and the payload.

Starting with *Discovery* STS-26, the clevis and tang design was deleted   and replaced with a *double-clevis, zero tolerance capture feature* that provided the structural stiffness to stabilize the joint during ignition and boost to SRB motor burnout.

Downplaying the purposes and accountability of meaningful rules and procedures is the adoption of recklessness, malpractice, and disservice.

I CONCLUDE THAT THE *FAILURE* WAS THE INADEQUATE STIFFNESS OF THE SRB JOINT STRUCTURE WHERE THE O-RINGS WERE CAPTIVE. THE *MALFUNCTION* WAS THE SUBSTANDARD SEALING PERFORMANCE OF THE SRB O-RINGS THAT RESULTED IN HOT GAS BLOW-BY AND IMPINGEMENT EROSION OF THE O-RING MATERIAL. PROPERLY INSTALLED O-RINGS COULD ONLY MALFUNCTION WHEN THE SRB JOINTS FLEXED BEYOND SAFE LIMITS AT THE PERIOD OF TIME DURING IGNITION, LIFTOFF, AND BOOST THROUGH THE EARTH'S ATMOSPHERE. THE COLD TEMPERATURE EFFECTS ON THE SYNTHETIC O-RING MATERIAL ONLY EXACERBATED THE SEAL MALFUNCTION. IMPROPER SEATING OF O-RINGS AMPLIFIES THE EFFECTS OF JOINT ROTATION UPON O-RINGS.

The combination of the failure and the malfunction produced severe leaks from the SRB segment joints that quickly became larger due to the melting away of the steel of the SRB casings. The deterioration of the SRB casings allowed the 6,000°F SRB flame to impinge upon the massive steel linkages that attached the SRB to the External Fuel Tank (ET), as well as the thin-walled aluminum structure of the ET. The temperatures exceeded the thermal limits of the steel and aluminum Space Shuttle components by factors of three and six, respectively. This thermal condition rapidly weakened the capability of the ET to carry structural loads. The heat from the leaking SRB flame also caused the failure of the critical weld seam that attaches the ET's lower dome structure to the cylinder-shaped portion of the ET. The failure of that weld seam allowed the total dumping of the liquid hydrogen fuel from the ET.

As the SRB to ET rear attach linkages failed, that released the thrusting end of the SRB and the entire SRB impulsively rotated about the massive forward SRB to ET attach fitting. The pointed tip of the SRB then penetrated the side of the ET at the liquid oxygen oxidizer section.

As the SRB to ET structural dynamic failure sequences were occurring, the three points where the Orbiter was attached to the ET began to diverge out of their geometric plane.   This out-of-plane dynamic motion introduced severe bending moment and shearing forces upon the fuselage of the Orbiter. Those forces on the Orbiter combined with the aerodynamic loading that was due to the Orbiter's high angles of attack that quickly developed at the 1,700 miles per hour speed through the air. The end result was that the Orbiter *Challenger* was destroyed in about two seconds. When people discuss the *Challenger* crash, they should realize the difference in the failure and the malfunction, and they should realize that the *Challenger* did not "explode," but rather was shredded when the Space Shuttle's attitude deviated from the trajectory flight path and was aerodynamically stressed to beyond the design limits.

In Volume I, Chapter VII, The Commission's Report <u>actually states what the true faulty design of the SRB was, but the report continues and erroneously condemns the SRB field joint O-rings to be the failed component instead of the structural stiffness of the SRB steel casing that caused excessive joint rotation during ignition and SRB burn.</u> The design changes that solved the O-ring malfunction problems were primarily changes to the SRB steel casing geometry and assembly procedures.   In addition, the O-ring design was reviewed and modified for geometric fit and function in the joint.   An additional O-ring was added for redundancy to total three O-rings in the final redesign. The O-rings never were, and are not now, designed to hold back the extreme temperatures of the SRB combustion gases and thermal radiation.

If you are not yet convinced that the SRB steel casing clevis and tang joints were the <u>FAILURE</u> of the SRB that caused the *Challenger* to crash and almost caused the crash of many previous Space Shuttle flights, then consider the following NASA and contractor memos and letters regarding the SRB joint structures and O-ring performance problems from 1977 to 1986:

1.   The 1977 NASA MSFC Internal Memo, *SRM Clevis Joint Leakage Study*. This is the earliest known indication that the SRB joint was unacceptable. I was a senior college student at the time at Georgia Tech. Four years later we had built Space Shuttle *Columbia* and launched STS-1 on April 12, 1981.

2.   The January 9, 1978 MSFC Internal Memo (Miller to Eudy), *Restatement of Position on SRM Clevis Joint O-Ring Acceptance Criteria and Clevis Joint Shim Requirements,* in which Mr. Miller was pleading to gain support for proper shim sizing and highest quality O-ring materials.

3.   The January 19, 1979 MSFC Internal Memo (Miller to Eudy), *Evaluation of SRM Clevis Joint Behavior,* documents SRM clevis joint high pressure O-ring seals test results to be unsatisfactory and calls for comments and questions to be referred to Mr. William L. Ray.   VERY IMPORTANT! *This Memo in items a. and b. date and document the Joint Rotation problem Failure Mode and occurrence.*
ITEM (A.) "The large sealing surface gap created by excessive tang/clevis relative movement causes the primary O-ring seal to extrude into the gap, forcing the seal to function in a way which violates industry and Government O-ring application practices."

ITEM (B.) "Excessive tang/clevis movement as explained above also allows the secondary O-ring seal to become completely disengaged from its sealing surface on the tang."

ITEM (C.) "Contract End Item Specification, CPWL-2500D, page I-28, paragraph 3.2.1.2 requires that the integrity of all high pressure case seals be verifiable; the clevis joint secondary O-ring seal has been verified by tests to be unsatisfactory."

4.   The February 6, 1979 MSFC Memo (Mr. Ray to Distribution), *Visit to Precision Rubber Products Corporation and Parker Seal Company,* that documents visit to Precision Rubber Products Corporation in Lebanon, TN and Parker Seal Company in Lexington, KY regarding the O-ring gaps experienced on SRB clevis joint tests. The visits were to seek opinions regarding potential risks involved. The Memo reported that Precision Rubber invested much time and effort in support of the problem even though they had no connection with the project. The Memo reported that Parker Seal showed a serious interest in assisting MSFC in solving the problem, but "Parker experts would make no reliability and potential risk factors associated with the design." The Memo states that Parker's "first thought was that the O-ring was being asked to perform beyond its intended design and that a different type of seal should be considered." The Memo also reported, "additional testing of the present design ... which more closely simulate actual conditions should be done."

5.   The original NASA *SRB Critical Items List*, establishes the SRB O-rings as Criticality 1R(redundant). The Critical Items List describes the O-ring functions, the groove requirements where the O-ring is installed, the

failure modes and failure effects of the O-ring. This document states the failure effect to be, "Loss of mission, vehicle, and crew due to probable case burst resulting in fire and deflagration."

6. The late 1982 MSFC Safety Reliability & Quality Assurance (SR&QA) engineers reviewed test and analysis results and determined that the case joints should be reclassified as Criticality 1 (not redundant). Mr. Maurice (Bud) Parker, a local Thiokol Reliability engineer, signed this form.   Mr. Parker's signature began the process of management's approval of the Criticality change.

7. The January 21, 1983 *MSFC (Level III) Configuration Control Board (CCB)*, chaired by Lawrence Mulloy, approved the SRB O-ring criticality change from Criticality 1R to Criticality 1 (no redundancy), and approved it for forwarding to Level II (JSC) for review and approval.

8. The 1983 *Space Shuttle Program Requirements Control Board (PRCB) Directive – Level II*, Shuttle Program Manager, Glynn Lunney, approved the Criticality change based upon a <u>*telephone call*</u> with Lawrence Mulloy, SRB Program Manager. The usual PRCB board meeting was not held. Lunney's approval authorized a waiver of the "fail safe" design requirement to be submitted to Level 1 (NASA Headquarters, Washington, DC) and was approved there by Michael Weeks on March 28, 1983.

9. The *MSFC Internal Memo,* written by John Miller to George Hardy and Mr. Coates, regarding O-ring erosion and "hot gas blow-by past the O-ring" experienced on STS 41B (flight 11), and raises concern for the safety of

the upcoming STS-13 flight.

10.   The March 9, 1984 United Technologies United Space Boosters Internal Correspondence, *zinc Chromate Putty in SRM Joints,* to Larry Mulloy of NASA, from George Morefield regarding the use of Zinc Chromate Putty in the SRM joints.   This correspondence documents discussions prior to March 9, 1984 that compare the *Titan III* rocket SRM history that is quite similar to the Shuttle SRM experience.   This memo refers to the Zinc Chromate putty used in the Shuttle and *Titan III* joints as *"Lucky Putty"* and that the Lucky Putty has always been surrounded by controversy regarding its performance and functional capabilities.   The memo warns of a higher failure probability for the Shuttle SRM joints indicating that the putty may cause single point pressurization of the primary O-ring.

11.   The January 13, 1985 Certified Urgent Message, *51C 0-RING EROSION RE: 51E FRR,* sent by Larry Mulloy to Larry Wear, SRM Manager, and passed on to Morton Thiokol as a direction to prepare a detailed briefing on O-ring problems for the next NASA Flight Rediness Review (FRR).

12.   The July 17, 1985 NASA Headquarters (Level 1) Memo, *Case to Case and Nozzle to Case "O" Ring Seal Erosion Problems,* from Mr. Irv Davids to Associate Administrator for Space Flight regarding Case-to-Case and Nozzle–to-Case O-ring Seal erosion problems.   This Memo documents Mr. Davids' visit to MSFC due to O-ring problems suffered by STS 51-B (flight 17).

13.   The July 31, 1985 Interoffice Memo of Morton Thiokol, *SRM 0-Ring Erosion/Potential Failure Criticality,*

from Roger M. Boisjoly (SRB engineer) to R. K. Lund (Vice President, Engineering, Morton Thiokol) regarding SRM O-ring erosion and potential failure criticality. The engineer argues and pleads that "the mistakenly accepted position on the joint problem" has now changed due to joint Primary O-ring blow-by of hot gases that caused erosion of the Secondary O-ring. The Memo documents that the clevis joint structure rotation is too quick for the O-ring to keep pace with and that if these design problems are not solved, then "we stand in jeopardy of losing a flight and the launch Pad facilities."

14. The August 22, 1985 Interoffice Memo of Morton Thiokol, *SRM Flight Seal Recommendation,* from A. R. Thompson, Supervisor Structures Design, to S. R. Stein, Project Engineer, regarding O-ring seal problems that had become "acute" and that short term solutions are being sought and that a near term solution should be incorporated following STS-27 (two flights after *Challenger* 51-L, or STS-25). This Memo was signed only five months before the *Challenger* Tragedy. An example of too little too late to prevent the Tragedy.

15. The October 1, 1985 Interoffice Memo of Morton Thiokol, *Weekly Activity Report 1 October 1985,* from Robert Ebeling, Manager of SRM Ignition Systems, Final Assembly, Special Projects, and Ground Test. This Memo literally pleads for "HELP!" and states, "The seal task force is constantly being delayed by every possible means. People are quoting policy and systems without work-around. MSFC is correct in stating that we do not know how to run a development program."

This is the pot calling the kettle black! NASA

was guilty of the same accusations. NASA was responsible for the contractor, but failed to achieve the expected and required performance with the contractors. With that failure of the NASA program management, NASA was in no trustworthy position to appraise the contractor's performance on the contract.

The evidence is overwhelming that the little O-ring was being rattled about by the dynamic motion of the SRB joint clevis and tang flexing during motor propellant burn. Because of this motion, the O-ring had little chance to be successful in the sealing function to hold back the Zinc Chromate "Lucky Putty" and indirectly the pressure and heat from the SRB combustion gases. The structure failed to perform its intended function and that caused the malfunction of the O-ring. The failure and the malfunction combined to produce the tragic crash of *Challenger.*

My job at NASA involved building, testing, and design change modifications to the Space Shuttle Orbiter. I became involved with engineering methods that analyze failure modes and the effects of those failures upon the safe operation of the Shuttle.

The primary structural frame and skins of the Orbiter were designed "not to fail." Failures of primary structure were always considered catastrophic. The Space Shuttle flights had to maintain the dynamic and static loads below the design limits of allowable stresses.

The mechanisms, on the other hand, did have failure modes that could yield undesirable effects upon the functions of those mechanical systems. Those potential failure conditions varied in severity, but the goal of all NASA efforts was to have no failures that could place the Astronauts at unacceptable risk levels.

The majority of my inputs to failure analysis

evolved from our work analyzing and repairing failed or damaged Orbiter components. That process of improving the Orbiter designs incorporated all disciplines and job functions of the space center team. The people who contributed to the Space Shuttle improvement work were engineers, technicians, safety personnel, and the very valuable quality control personnel. Contractors and NASA Civil Service workers were creative and productive in their attitudes and contributions to the team that has made the Space Shuttle a world record-setting program. Many times, those employees resorted to the Employee Suggestion system to get their ideas considered.

NASA's design philosophy for the Space Shuttle was much like the philosophy applied while designing the *Apollo Saturn V* Moon rocket. The Space Shuttle and *Apollo* launch vehicles were designed to have several backup systems to provide the function of the primary system if the primary failed. <u>The "redundancy" design philosophy is opposite from the "no single failure" design philosophy applied to modern commercial passenger aircraft.</u>

A contrasting example is the Federal Aviation Administration's (FAA) regulations which require commercial aircraft to be designed so that "<u>no single failure can result in loss of the continued safe flight and landing</u>" of the aircraft (Ref. 14 Code of Federal Regulations, Federal Aviation Regulations, Part 25.1309).

It is important to understand that "safety" is a relative measure that is completely determined by the risks, hazards, and exposures that are considered acceptable. The odds of a "safe" system becoming "unsafe" can be determined by the periods of time that a person is exposed to the risks and hazards of operating the design.   Design and maintenance directly control the level of safety.

Reliability simply means that a system or machine functions properly, as designed, when called upon to operate. We can see that safety and reliability are simple, but complex in application. Each of the Space Shuttle Astronauts had to study the Space Shuttle systems design, understand the hazards, risks and exposures, and then make a colossal decision as to whether or not the Space Shuttle was "safe" to fly.

The Astronauts of the 51-L mission did not voice their opinions loud enough regarding the weather conditions and problems that the weather presented to the launch countdown routine. A crew's reluctance to announce their decision not to participate in a launch due to adverse weather conditions is understandable. Since millions of people were watching, and since so many people had labored to prepare *Challenger* for launch, who would have the nerve to announce, "The crew has made a decision not to fly today?" The crew may have cheated themselves of a chance to stop the launch for adverse weather condition on that day. The crash may still have happened the next day, regardless if the crew had scrubbed the launch. The point is that any Commander must have the authority to respectfully not fly if they are certain that conditions do not warrant a safe flight and ride to orbit. Had there been propel-lants noticeably gushing from the Space Shuttle prior to launch, no crewmember would have agreed to fly that day.   If the Astronauts had known more about degraded performance of cold O-rings, or improperly installed O-rings, then they would not have flown that day.   If the Astronauts had understood that the steel casings of the SRBs were not stiff enough, then they would not have flown that day. So what if a launch scrub costs millions of dollars? Safety must be first in high performance rocketry.

I believe that most of the Astronauts of the *Mercury, Gemini,* and *Apollo* programs were motivated by the contest, the game of competing to be the best, the first to pilot a craft where no one has ever been. This behavior could be called the "higher, faster, farther" ambition. Many of the Astronauts today became Shuttle Astronauts because they were qualified and they wanted to "ride the rocket" and "see the Earth from up there."

A minority percentage of all Astronauts are "dyed-in-the-wool," confirmed explorers. Many of the Astronauts who are astronomers tend to be dedicated explorers. Telescopes used by explorers through the years have evolved from the old brass "telescoping" monocle designs and have improved to become the sophisticated "time travel machine" of the *Hubble Space Telescope (HST)*. Ancient exploration flourished with explorers who viewed the high seas, mountains, and plains with one eye squinted and the other eye peering into a low power telescope. Today, explorers use both eyes in three-dimensional stereovision. The true test that reveals how much of an explorer is in an Astronaut is by the type of work they do after they no longer fly the Space Shuttle.

NASA management was more effective in achieving the missions than many management organizations that exist in private business. But as the flights of Space Shuttles continued, NASA management did relax and expand their comfort zone that established which Shuttle vehicle configurations of design and maintenance would be safe for flight.

It is understandable how NASA management became authors of the "equation for disaster" by launching Space Shuttles with known design defects in the Solid Rocket Boosters. But before we condemn those NASA and contractor managers, we should consider the human tendency in many of us to "take the risk," especially when the potential gain is great. It is easy for us to imagine that we will, in some luck of probability, be immune to any dangers associated with the risks. People hope that the tragic outcomes are supposed to be only for the inanimate crash dummies that serve humanity in some virtual reality that cannot harm us.

Stay with me for a moment on safety analysis and the management decision-making process. I had the honor of working on the *Challenger* crash investigation team with the late physicist, Dr. Richard P. Feynman. While Feynman was considered by many to be eccentric and bizarre, I had the highest respect for him as a scientific colleague because of such skillful work as the following report that he wrote 1986. Submitted to the *Rogers Presidential Commission,* it has become what I consider to be the most valuable and applicable portion of the entire Presidential Report on the *Challenger* Accident Investigation.

The report is *Appendix F, Volume II, of The Presidential Report on The Space Shuttle Challenger Accident.* Dr. Feynman was in a position on the Commission to deliver in writing what I know to be the reality of how humans behave when events are repeated with apparent success.

Humans develop an "artificial intelligence" that the next attempt of a risky venture will be safe and successful. We are likely to ignore the hazards, risks, and exposures in some proportional function to the increasing number of successful attempts of risky ventures.

Most people will never read or scan through the five volumes of the *Challenger* Accident Report. I have included Appendix F in this book. I believe that Dr. Feynman has given us a tool of guidance for aerospace program managers, government officials, financial investors, and concerned citizens to evaluate the safety and reliability of space exploration programs and for public trusted programs such as public transportation and public health.

APPENDIX F - PERSONAL OBSERVATIONS ON THE RELIABILITY OF THE SHUTTLE

By R. P. Feynman

INTRODUCTION

"It appears that there are enormous differences of opinion as to the probability of a failure with loss of vehicle and of human life. The estimates range from roughly 1 in 100 to 1 in 100,000. The higher figures come from the working engineers, and the very low figures from management. What are the causes and consequences of this lack of agreement? Since 1 part in 100,000 would imply that one could put a Shuttle up each day for 300 years expecting to lose only one, we could properly ask "What is the cause of management's fantastic faith in the machinery?"

We have also found that certification criteria used in Flight Readiness Reviews often develop a gradually decreasing strictness. The argument that the same risk was flown before without failure is often accepted as an argument for the safety of accepting it again. Because of this, obvious weaknesses are accepted again and again, sometimes without a sufficiently serious attempt to remedy them, or to delay a flight because of their continued presence.

There are several sources of information. There are published criteria for certification, including a history of modifications in the form of waivers and deviations. In addition, the records of the Flight Readiness Reviews for each flight document the arguments used to accept the risks of the flight. Information was obtained from the direct testimony and the reports of the range safety officer, Louis J. Ullian, with respect to the history of success of solid fuel rockets. There was a further study by him (as chairman of the launch abort safety panel (LASP)) in an attempt to determine the risks involved in possible accidents leading to radioactive contamination from attempting to fly a plutonium power supply (RTG) for future planetary missions. The NASA study of the same question is also available. For the History of the Space Shuttle Main Engines, interviews with management and engineers at Marshall, and informal interviews with engineers at Rocketdyne, were made. An independent (Cal Tech) mechanical engineer who consulted for NASA about engines was also interviewed informally. A visit to Johnson was made to gather information on the reliability of the avionics (computers, sensors, and effectors). Finally there is a report "A Review of Certification Practices, Potentially Applicable to Man-rated Reusable Rocket Engines," prepared at the Jet Propulsion Laboratory by N. Moore, et al., in February, 1986, for NASA Headquarters, Office of Space Flight. It deals with the methods used by the FAA and the military to certify their gas turbine and rocket engines. These authors were also interviewed informally.

SOLID ROCKETS (SRB)

The range safety officer made an estimate of the reliability of solid rockets by studying the experience of all previous rocket flights. Out of a total of nearly 2,900 flights, 121 failed (1 in 25). This includes, however, what may be called, early errors, rockets flown for the first few times in which design errors are discovered and fixed. A more reasonable figure for the mature rockets might be 1 in 50. With special care in the selection of parts and in inspection, a figure of below 1 in 100 might be achieved but 1 in 1,000 is probably not attainable with today's technology. (Since there are two rockets on the Shuttle, these rocket failure rates must be doubled to get Shuttle failure rates from Solid Rocket Booster failure.)

NASA officials argue that the figure is much lower. They point out that these figures are for unmanned rockets but since the Shuttle is a manned vehicle "the probability of mission success is necessarily very close to 1.0." It is not very clear what this phrase means. Does it mean it is close to 1 or that it ought to be close to

1? They go on to explain "Historically this extremely high degree of mission success has given rise to a difference in philosophy between manned space flight programs and unmanned programs; i.e., numerical probability usage versus engineering judgment." (These quotations are from "Space Shuttle Data for Planetary Mission RTG Safety Analysis," Pages 3-1, 3-1, February 15, 1985, NASA, JSC.) It is true that if the probability of failure was as low as 1 in 100,000 it would take an inordinate number of tests to determine it (you would get nothing but a string of perfect flights from which no precise figure, other than that the probability is likely less than the number of such flights in the string so far). But, if the real probability were not so small, flights would show troubles, near failures, and possible actual failures with a reasonable number of trials. A standard statistical method could give a reasonable estimate. In fact, previous NASA experience had shown, on occasion, just such difficulties, near accidents, and accidents, all giving warning that the probability of flight failure was not so very small. The inconsistency of the argument not to determine reliability through historical experience, as the range safety officer did, is that NASA also appeals to history, beginning "Historically this high degree of mission success..."

Finally, if we are to replace standard numerical probability usage with engineering judgment, why do we find such an enormous disparity between the management estimate and the judgment of the engineers? It would appear that, for whatever purpose, be it for internal or external consumption, the management of NASA exaggerates the reliability of its product, to the point of fantasy.

The history of the certification and Flight Readiness Reviews will not be repeated here. (See other part of Commission reports.) The phenomenon of accepting for flight, seals that had shown erosion and blow-by in previous flights, is very clear. The *Challenger* flight is an excellent example. There are several references to flights that had gone before. The acceptance and success of these flights is taken as evidence of safety. But erosion and blow-by are not what the design expected. They are warnings that something is wrong. The equipment is not operating as expected, and therefore there is a danger that it can operate with even wider deviations in this unexpected and not thoroughly understood way. The fact that this danger did not lead to a catastrophe before is no guarantee that it will not the next time, unless it is completely understood. When playing Russian roulette the fact that the first shot got off safely is little comfort for the next. The origin and consequences of the erosion and blow-by were not understood. They did not occur equally on all flights and all joints; sometimes more, and sometimes less. Why not sometime, when whatever conditions determined it were right, still more leading to catastrophe?

In spite of these variations from case to case, officials behaved as if they understood it, giving apparently logical arguments to each other often depending on the "success" of previous flights. For example, in determining if the flight 51-L was safe to fly in the face of ring erosion in flight 51-C, it was noted that the erosion depth was only one-third of the radius. It had been noted in an experiment cutting the ring that cutting it as deep as one radius was necessary before the ring failed. Instead of being very concerned that variations of poorly understood conditions might reasonably create deeper erosion this time, it was asserted, there was "a safety factor of three." This is a strange use of the engineer's term," safety factor." If a bridge is built to withstand a certain load without the beams permanently deforming, cracking, or breaking, it may be designed for the materials used to actually stand up under three times the load. This "safety factor" is to allow for uncertain excesses of load, or unknown extra loads, or weaknesses in the material that might have unexpected flaws, etc. If now the expected load comes on to the new bridge and a crack appears in a beam, this is a failure of the design. There was no safety factor at all; even though the bridge did not actually collapse because the crack went only one-third of the way through the beam. The O-rings of the Solid Rocket Boosters were not designed to erode. Erosion was a clue that something was wrong. Erosion was not something from which safety can be inferred.

There was no way, without full understanding, that one could have confidence that conditions the next time might not produce erosion three times more severe than the time before. Nevertheless, officials fooled themselves into thinking they had such understanding and confidence, in spite of the peculiar variations from case to case. A mathematical model was made to calculate erosion. This was a model based not on physical understanding but on empirical curve fitting. To be more detailed, it was supposed a stream of hot gas impinged on the O-ring material, and the heat was determined at the point of stagnation (so far, with reasonable physical, thermodynamic laws). But to determine how much rubber eroded it was assumed this depended only on this heat by a formula suggested by data on a similar material. A logarithmic plot suggested a straight line, so it was supposed that the erosion varied as the .58 power of the heat, the .58 being determined by a nearest fit. At any rate, adjusting some other numbers, it was determined that the model agreed with the erosion (to depth of one-third the radius of the ring). There is nothing much so wrong with this as believing the answer! Uncertainties appear everywhere. How strong the gas stream might be was unpredictable, it depended on holes formed in the putty. Blow-by showed that the ring might fail even though not, or only partially eroded through. The empirical formula was known to be uncertain, for it did not go directly through the very data points by which it was determined. There were a cloud of points some twice above, and some twice below the fitted curve, so erosions twice predicted were reasonable from that cause alone. Similar uncertainties surrounded the other constants in the formula, etc., etc. When using a mathematical model careful attention must be given to uncertainties in the model.

LIQUID FUEL ENGINE (SSME)

During the flight of 51-L the three Space Shuttle Main Engines all worked perfectly, even, at the last moment, beginning to shut down the engines as the fuel supply began to fail. The question arises, however, as to whether, had it failed, and we were to investigate it in as much detail as we did the Solid Rocket Booster, we would find a similar lack of attention to faults and a deteriorating reliability. In other words, were the organization weaknesses that contributed to the accident confined to the Solid Rocket Booster sector or were they a more general characteristic of NASA? To that end the Space Shuttle Main Engines and the avionics were both investigated. No similar study of the Orbiter, or the External Tank were made.

The engine is a much more complicated structure than the Solid Rocket Booster, and a great deal more detailed engineering goes into it. Generally, the engineering seems to be of high quality and apparently considerable attention is paid to deficiencies and faults found in operation.

The usual way that such engines are designed (for military or civilian aircraft) may be called the component system, or bottom-up design. First it is necessary to thoroughly understand the properties and limitations of the materials to be used (for turbine blades, for example), and tests are begun in experimental rigs to determine those. With this knowledge larger component parts (such as bearings) are designed and tested individually. As deficiencies and design errors are noted they are corrected and verified with further testing. Since one tests only parts at a time these tests and modifications are not overly expensive. Finally one works up to the final design of the entire engine, to the necessary specifications. There is a good chance, by this time that the engine will generally succeed, or that any failures are easily isolated and analyzed because the failure modes, limitations of materials, etc., are so well understood. There is a very good chance that the modifications to the engine to get around the final difficulties are not very hard to make, for most of the serious problems have already been discovered and dealt with in the earlier, less expensive, stages of the process.

The Space Shuttle Main Engine was handled in a different manner, top down, we might say. The engine was designed and put together all at once with relatively little detailed preliminary study of the material and components. Then when troubles are found in the bearings, turbine blades, coolant pipes, etc., it is more expensive and difficult to discover the causes and make changes. For example, cracks have been found in the turbine blades of the high-pressure oxygen turbo pump. Are they caused by flaws in the material, the effect of the oxygen atmosphere on the properties of the material, the thermal stresses of startup or shutdown, the vibration and stresses of steady running, or mainly at some resonance at certain speeds, etc.? How long can we run from crack initiation to crack failure, and how does this depend on power level? Using the completed engine as a test bed to resolve such questions is extremely expensive. One does not wish to lose an entire engine in order to find out where and how failure occurs. Yet, an accurate knowledge of this information is essential to acquire a confidence in the engine reliability in use. Without detailed understanding, confidence cannot be attained.

A further disadvantage of the top-down method is that, if an understanding of a fault is obtained, a simple fix, such as a new shape for the turbine housing, may be impossible to implement without a redesign of the entire engine.

The Space Shuttle Main Engine is a very remarkable machine. It has a greater ratio of thrust to weight than any previous engine. It is built at the edge of, or outside of, previous engineering experience. Therefore, as expected, many different kinds of flaws and difficulties have turned up. Because, unfortunately, it was built in the top-down manner, they are difficult to find and fix. The design aim of a lifetime of 55 missions' equivalent firings (27,000 seconds of operation, either in a mission of 500 seconds, or on a test stand) has not been obtained. The engine now requires very frequent maintenance and replacement of important parts, such as turbopumps, bearings, sheet metal housings, etc. The high-pressure fuel turbopump had to be replaced every three or four mission equivalents (although that may have been fixed, now) and the high-pressure oxygen turbopump every five or six. This is at most ten percent of the original specification. But our main concern here is the determination of reliability.

In a total of about 250,000 seconds of operation, the engines have failed seriously perhaps 16 times. Engineering pays close attention to these failings and tries to remedy them as quickly as possible. This it does by test studies on special rigs experimentally designed for the flaws in question, by careful inspection of the engine for suggestive clues (like cracks), and by considerable study and analysis. In this way, in spite of the difficulties of top-down design, through hard work, many of the problems have apparently been solved.

A list of some of the problems follows. Those followed by an asterisk (*) are probably solved:

1. Turbine blade cracks in high-pressure fuel turbopumps (HPFTP). (May have been solved.)

2. Turbine blade cracks in high-pressure oxygen turbopumps (HPOTP).

3. Augmented Spark Igniter (ASI) line rupture.*

4. Purge check valve failure.*

5. ASI chamber erosion.*

6. HPFTP turbine sheet metal cracking.

7. HPFTP coolant liner failure.*

8. Main combustion chamber outlet elbow failure.*

9. Main combustion chamber inlet elbow weld offset.*

10. HPOTP subsynchronous whirl.*

11. Flight acceleration safety cutoff system (partial failure in a redundant system).*

12. Bearing spalling (partially solved).

13. A vibration at 4,000 Hertz making some engines inoperable, etc.

Many of these solved problems are the early difficulties of a new design, for 13 of them occurred in the first 25,000 seconds and only three in the second 125,000 seconds. Naturally, one can never be sure that all the bugs are out, and, for some, the fix may not have addressed the true cause. Thus, it is not unreasonable to guess here may be at least one surprise in the next 250,000 seconds, a probability of 1/500 per engine per mission. On a mission there are three engines, but some accidents would possibly be contained, and only affect one engine. The system can abort with only two engines. Therefore let us say that the unknown surprises do not, even of themselves, permit us to guess that the probability of mission failure do to the Space Shuttle Main Engine is less than 1/500. To this we must add the chance of failure from known, but as yet unsolved, problems (those without the asterisk in the list above). These we discuss below. (Engineers at Rocketdyne, the manufacturer, estimate the total probability as 1/10,000. Engineers at marshal estimate it as 1/300, while NASA management, to whom these engineers report, claims it is 1/100,000. An independent engineer consulting for NASA thought 1 or 2 per 100 a reasonable estimate.)

The history of the certification principles for these engines is confusing and difficult to explain. Initially the rule seems to have been that two sample engines must each have had twice the time operating without failure as the operating time of the engine to be certified (rule of 2x). At least that is the FAA practice, and NASA seems to have adopted it, originally expecting the certified time to be 10 missions (hence 20 missions for each sample). Obviously the best engines to use for comparison would be those of greatest total (flight plus test) operating time — the so-called "fleet leaders." But what if a third sample and several others fail in a short time? Surely we will not be safe because two were unusual in lasting longer. The short time might be more representative of the real possibilities, and in the spirit of the safety factor of 2, we should only operate at half the time of the short-lived samples.

The slow shift toward decreasing safety factor can be seen in many examples. We take that of the HPFTP turbine blades. First of all the idea of testing an entire engine was abandoned. Each engine number has had many important parts (like the turbopumps themselves) replaced at frequent intervals, so that the rule must be shifted from engines to components. We accept an HPFTP for a certification time if two samples have each run successfully for twice that time (and of course, as a practical matter, no longer insisting that this time be as large as 10 missions). But what is "successfully?" The FAA calls a turbine blade crack a failure, in order, in practice, to really provide a safety factor greater than 2. There is some time that an engine can run between the time a crack originally starts until the time it has grown large enough to fracture. (The FAA is contemplating new rules that take this extra safety time into account, but only if it is very carefully analyzed through known models within a known range of experience and with materials thoroughly tested. None of these conditions apply to the Space Shuttle Main Engine.)

Cracks were found in many second stage HPFTP turbine blades. In one case three were found after 1,900 seconds, while in another they were not found after 4,200 seconds, although usually these longer runs showed cracks. To follow this story further we shall have to realize that the stress depends a great deal on the power level. The *Challenger* flight was to be at, and previous flights had been at, a power level called 104% of rated power level during most of the time the engines were operating. Judging from some material data it is supposed that at the level 104% of rated power level, the time to crack is about twice that at 109% or full power level (FPL). Future flights were to be at this level because of heavier payloads, and many tests were made at this level. Therefore dividing time at 104% by 2, we obtain units called equivalent full power level (EFPL). Obviously, some uncertainty is introduced by that, but it has not been studied.) The earliest cracks mentioned above occurred at 1,375 EFPL.

Now the certification rule becomes "limit all second stage blades to a maximum of 1,375 seconds EFPL." If one objects that the safety factor of 2 is lost it is pointed out that the one turbine ran for 3,800 seconds EFPL without cracks, and half of this is 1,900 so we are being more conservative. We have fooled ourselves in three ways. First we have only one sample, and it is not the fleet leader, for the other two samples of 3,800 or more seconds had 17 cracked blades between them. (There are 59 blades in the engine.) Next we have abandoned the 2x rule and substituted equal time. And finally, 1,375 is where we did see a crack. We can say that no crack had been found below 1,375, but the last time we looked and saw no cracks was 1,100 seconds EFPL. We do not know when the crack formed between these times, for example cracks may have formed at 1,150 seconds EFPL. (Approximately 2/3 of the blade sets tested in excess of 1,375 seconds EFPL had cracks. Some recent experiments have, indeed, shown cracks as early as 1,150 seconds.) It was important to keep the number high, for the *Challenger* was to fly an engine very close to the limit by the time the flight was over.

Finally it is claimed that the criteria are not abandoned, and the system is safe, by giving up the FAA convention that there should be no cracks, and considering only a completely fractured blade a failure. With this definition no engine has yet failed. The idea is that since there is sufficient time for a crack to grow to a fracture we can insure that all is safe by inspecting all blades for cracks. If they are found, replace them, and if none are found we have enough time for a safe mission. This makes the crack problem not a flight safety problem, but merely a maintenance problem.

This may in fact be true. But how well do we know that cracks always grow slowly enough that no fracture can occur in a mission? Three engines have run for long times with a few cracked blades (about 3,000 seconds EFPL) with no blades broken off.

But a fix for this cracking may have been found. By changing the blade shape, shot-peening the surface, and covering with insulation to exclude thermal shock, the blades have not cracked so far.

A very similar story appears in the history of certification of the HPOTP, but we shall not give the details here.

It is evident, in summary, that the Flight Readiness Reviews and certification rules show a deterioration for some of the problems of the Space Shuttle Main Engine that is closely analogous to the deterioration seen in the rules for the Solid Rocket Booster.

AVIONICS

By "avionics" is meant the computer system on the Orbiter as well as its input sensors and output actuators. At first we will restrict ourselves to the computers proper and not be concerned with the reliability of the input information from the sensors of temperature, pressure, etc., nor with whether the computer output is faithfully followed by the actuators of rocket firings, mechanical controls, displays to Astronauts, etc.

The computer system is very elaborate, having over 250,000 lines of code. It is responsible, among many other things, for the automatic control of the entire ascent to orbit, and for the descent until well into the atmosphere (below Mach 1) once one button is pushed deciding the landing site desired. It would be possible to make the entire landing automatically (except that the landing gear lowering signal is expressly left out of computer control, and must be provided by the pilot, ostensibly for safety reasons) but such an entirely automatic landing is probably not as safe as a pilot controlled landing. During orbital flight it is used in the control of payloads, in displaying information to the Astronauts, and the exchange of information to the ground. It is evident that the safety of flight requires guaranteed accuracy of this elaborate system of computer hardware and software.

In brief, the hardware reliability is ensured by having four essentially independent identical computer systems. Where possible each sensor also has multiple copies, usually four, and each copy feeds all four of the computer lines. If the inputs from the sensors disagree, depending on circumstances, certain averages, or a majority selection is used as the effective input. The algorithm used by each of the four computers is exactly the same, so their inputs (since each sees all copies of the sensors) are the same. Therefore at each step the results in each computer should be identical. From time to time they are compared, but because they might operate at slightly different speeds a system of stopping and waiting at specific times is instituted before each comparison is made. If one of the computers disagrees, or is too late in having its answer ready, the three which do agree are assumed to be correct and the errant computer is taken completely out of the system. If, now, another computer fails, as judged by the agreement of the other two, it is taken out of the system, and the rest of the flight canceled, and descent to the landing site is instituted, controlled by the two remaining computers. It is seen that this is a redundant system since the failure of only one computer does not affect the mission. Finally, as an extra feature of safety, there is a fifth independent computer, whose memory is loaded with only the programs of ascent and descent, and which is capable of controlling the descent if there is a failure of more than two of the computers of the main line four.

There is not enough room in the memory of the main line computers for all the programs of ascent, descent, and payload programs in flight, so the memory is loaded about four times from tapes, by the Astronauts.

Because of the enormous effort required to replace the software for such an elaborate system, and for checking a new system out, no change has been made to the hardware since the system began about fifteen years ago. The actual hardware is obsolete; for example, the memories are of the old ferrite core type. It is becoming more difficult to find manufacturers to supply such old-fashioned computers reliably and of high quality. Modern computers are very much more reliable, can run much faster, simplifying circuits, and allowing more to be done, and would not require so much loading of memory, for the memories are much larger.

The software is checked very carefully in a bottom-up fashion. First, each new line of code is checked, then sections of code or modules with special functions are verified. The scope is increased step by step until the new changes are incorporated into a complete system and checked. This complete output is considered the final product, newly released. But completely independently there is an independent verification group, that takes an adversary attitude to the software development group, and tests and verifies the software as if it were a customer of the delivered product. There is additional verification in using the new programs in simulators, etc. A discovery of an error during verification testing is considered very serious, and its origin studied very carefully to avoid such mistakes in the future. Such unexpected errors have been found only about six times in all the programming and program changing (for new or altered payloads) that has been done. The principle that is followed is that all the verification is not an aspect of program safety, it is merely a test of that safety, in a non-catastrophic verification. Flight safety is to be judged solely on how well the programs do in the verification tests. A failure here generates considerable concern.

To summarize then, the computer software checking system and attitude is of the highest quality. There appears to be no process of gradually fooling oneself while degrading standards so characteristic of the Solid Rocket Booster or Space Shuttle Main Engine safety systems. To be sure, there have been recent suggestions by management to curtail such elaborate and expensive tests as being unnecessary at this late date in Shuttle history. This must be resisted for it does not appreciate the mutual subtle influences, and sources of errors generated by even small changes of one part of a program on another. There are perpetual requests for changes as new payloads and new demands and modifications are suggested by the users. Changes are expensive because they require extensive testing. The proper way to save money is to curtail the number of requested changes, not the quality of testing for each.

One might add that the elaborate system could be very much improved by more modern hardware and programming techniques. Any outside competition would have all the advantages of starting over, and whether that is a good idea for NASA now should be carefully considered.

Finally, returning to the sensors and actuators of the avionics system, we find that the attitude to system failure and reliability is not nearly as good as for the computer system. For example, a difficulty was found with certain temperature sensors sometimes failing. Yet 18 months later the same sensors were still being used, still sometimes failing, until a launch had to be scrubbed because two of them failed at the same time. Even on a succeeding flight this unreliable sensor was used again. Again reaction control systems, the rocket jets used for reorienting and control in flight still are somewhat unreliable. There is considerable redundancy, but a long history of failures, none of which has yet been extensive enough to seriously affect flight. The action of the jets is checked by sensors, and, if they fail to fire the computers choose another jet to fire. But they are not designed to fail, and the problem should be solved.

Conclusions

If a reasonable launch schedule is to be maintained, engineering often cannot be done fast enough to keep up with the expectations of originally conservative certification criteria designed to guarantee a very safe vehicle. In these situations, subtly, and often with apparently logical arguments, the criteria are altered so that flights may still be certified in time. They therefore fly in a relatively unsafe condition, with a chance of failure of the order of a percent (it is difficult to be more accurate).

Official management, on the other hand, claims to believe the probability of failure is a thousand times less. One reason for this may be an attempt to assure the government of NASA perfection and success in order to ensure the supply of funds. The other may be that they sincerely believed it to be true, demonstrating an almost incredible lack of communication between themselves and their working engineers.

In any event this has had very unfortunate consequences, the most serious of which is to encourage ordinary citizens to fly in such a dangerous machine, as if it had attained the safety of an ordinary airliner. The Astronauts, like test pilots, should know their risks, and we honor them for their courage. Who can doubt that McAuliffe was equally a person of great courage, who was closer to an awareness of the true risk than NASA management would have us believe?

Let us make recommendations to ensure that NASA officials deal in a world of reality in understanding technological weaknesses and imperfections well enough to be actively trying to eliminate them. They must live in reality in comparing the costs and utility of the Shuttle to other methods of entering space. And they must be realistic in making contracts, in estimating costs, and the difficulty of the projects. Only realistic flight schedules should be proposed, or schedules that have a reasonable chance of being met. If in this way the government would not support them, then so be it. NASA owes it to the citizens from whom it asks support to be frank, honest, and informative, so that these citizens can make the wisest decisions for the use of their limited resources.

FOR A SUCCESSFUL TECHNOLOGY, REALITY MUST TAKE PRECEDENCE OVER PUBLIC RELATIONS, FOR NATURE CANNOT BE FOOLED."

{The is the End of the text for Dr. Feynman's Letter to NASA Management.}

(Source: The Presidential Commission on the Space Shuttle *Challenger* Accident Report, June 6, 1986, Appendix F)

I must amplify three conclusions that Dr. Feynman made because our society includes a government/industry hate-love relationship, each struggling for the upper hand of power and control over the other.   Neither entity is content with possessing just the right amount of power to balance the system.   Each entity lusts for just a little more power and control. Dr. Feynman was very accurate and courageous in stating the following points which I believe that all of us in government service and in privately owned and operated industry must always remember as we manage or work for our companies:

> *"In these situations, subtly, and often with apparently logical arguments, the criteria are altered so that flights may still be certified in time. They therefore fly in a relatively unsafe condition, with a chance of failure of the order of a percent (it is difficult to be more accurate).*

*The other may be that they sincerely
believed it to be true, demonstrating an almost
incredible lack of communication between themselves
and their working engineers.*

*In any event this has had very unfortunate
consequences, the most serious of which is to encourage
ordinary citizens to fly in such a dangerous machine,
as if it had attained the safety of an ordinary
airliner."*

Dr. Feynman was very correct. I have summarized in my own words and experiences three simple rules that if followed will allow the greatest probability of continued success with any kind of program, business plan, or strategy:

THREE SIMPLE RULES TO WORK BY:

1. **DEVELOP REALISTIC AND MEANINGFUL RULES AND COMPLY TO THE RULES.**
2. **MANAGERS AND WORKERS MUST COMMUNICATE IN RELIABLE WAYS THAT DO NOT FOSTER FEAR OR DISINTEGRATION OF TRUST.**
3. **MARKET THE SAFETY AND RELIABILITY OF YOUR PRODUCTS ACCURATELY SO THAT YOU AND YOUR CUSTOMERS CAN ESTABLISH HONEST EXPECTATIONS. A CUSTOMER KILLED BY A FAULTY PRODUCT WILL NEVER BUY FROM YOU AGAIN.**

I hear your gripes about Rule 1. Calm down, calm down. I realize that in private sector the "rule" seems to be "make the sale no matter what." In that lifestyle, the Rule is: "There are no rules." A company that functions with essentially no rules is a company with a litigation nightmare on its horizon. The point is that government and private sector must have written rules and procedures for operations *and follow the rules*. If the rules are outdated or flawed in some way, *change the rules* by the official procedures of the company or government authority.   Why should any CEO be hanging out in the firestorm alone simply because the CEO wants to be a maverick cowgirl or cowboy and make up their own rules day-by-day? Why should any employee of a company or government authority risk losing their career and paycheck, and in a great act of disloyalty, risk the company's product, reputation, and business plan simply because the employee wanted to be a maverick by determining their own "rules du jour".   The employee was hired to produce product, and that process usually includes company rules and procedures.

A company or a government authority that will-fully adapts a lifestyle of fabricating their own blend of "rules du jour" is in fact a fraud of business practice and a hypocrite of ethics and judgment. Successful entre-preneurs don't run their businesses wrecklessly. They have clear and simple business plans and procedures (rules), they communicate reliably, and they market their products by <u>under</u> committing and <u>over</u> deliv-ering.   Organizations operated "sans les rules", or without meaningful rules, have by default judged their customers and innocent bystanders to be fools who will tolerate any performance or accident. All govern-ment entities and private companies have the choice to live one lifestyle or the other. Change from fraudulent to legitimate operations is honorable.   Endorsement and propagation of fraudulent operations is dishonor-able and cheats the world.

"IN FLYING I HAVE LEARNED THAT CARELESSNESS and OVERCONFIDENCE ARE USUALLY FAR MORE DANGEROUS THAN DELIBERATELY ACCEPTED RISKS."

Orville Wright

"AVIATION IN ITSELF IS NOT INHERENTLY DANGER-OUS. BUT TO AN EVEN GREATER DEGREE THAN THE SEA, IT IS TERRIBLY UNFORGIVING OF ANY CARELESS-NESS, INCAPACITY OR NEGLECT."

Captain A. G. Lamplugh
British Aviation Insurance Group, London.
(Circa early 1930s)

"OF THE MAJOR INCENTIVES TO IMPROVE SAFETY, BY FAR THE MOST COMPELLING IS THAT OF ECONOMICS. THE MORAL INCENTIVE, WHICH IS MOST EVIDENT FOLLOWING AN ACCIDENT, IS MORE INTENSE BUT IS RELATIVELY SHORT LIVED."

Jerome Lederer

"I AM A HISTORY MAJOR. I BELIEVE THAT THE PAST IS PROLOGUE. THE ARCHIVES BEAR THAT OUT. MOST MAJOR AIRCRAFT ACCIDENTS ARE NOT ACTS OF GOD. IN OUR RECOMMENDATIONS WE TRY TO TAKE WHAT WE HAVE LEARNED AND CORRECT SITUATIONS SO IT SHOULDN'T HAPPEN AGAIN."

James Hall, Chairman, National Transportation Safety Board, USA, 1996.

CHAPTER 16

PRESIDENT REAGAN'S STATE OF THE UNION ADDRESS - AND *Challenger*

The United States Constitution, Article II, Section 3, requires of the President of the United States, "He shall from time to time give to the Congress *Information of the State of the Union*, and recommend to their consideration such measures as he shall judge necessary and expedient." The tradition of today includes the act of passing information about the state of the Union by presenting a meticulously prepared speech that is presented in person by the President to the Joint Session of Congress that includes both the House of Representatives and the Senate memberships. Americans refer to this annual speech presentation as *"The State of the Union Address to the Nation."*

This Constitutional requirement not only brings the House of Representatives and Senate members to the same chamber of lawmaking for the evening, but many other appointed government officials are formally invited to attend. Those government-appointed officials include the President's Cabinet officers, or Secretaries, the military services Joint Chiefs of Staff, and selected Governors of states.

This evening get-together in the nation's Capitol Building has evolved into a President's political transfusion medium to attempt to show the President's party performance as successful and worthy of reelection to office when the next election occurs. Viewers watching by television closely watch the human behaviors of those in attendance. Smiles, applause, winks, nods of the head, and body language reminiscent of a third base coach in baseball are part of the show. It is a show that is produced and broadcast like any profes- sionally broadcast television show. There is nothing particularly wrong with taking advantage of the Constitutional requirement, or the technologies of tele- vision and satellite communications, but it does seem to provide the President in office with an emotional platform from which to sway or convince the viewers to believe and support the party "planks" of the party "platform". The Constitution was written in horse and buggy days and did not place any presentation guide- lines upon the report to Congress from the President.

It is significant to understand that it was the authors of the U.S. Constitution who required the President to report to Congress the state, or condition of the Union. It was not realistic or practical to require the President to report to the population at large because of the limited communications systems avail- able during the 18th and 19th Centuries. The Congressional members were elected to represent the citizens in lawmaking, relate the news to their constituents back home, and to make responsible deci- sions for legislation of laws on the people's behalf.

Today's technologies and cosmetic presentation of the President is savvy and a game of political psychology. Convincing millions of people that all is well in government and that the officials in power are worthy of another term in office is a daunting challenge to anyone. It is historic that American politicians have reinvented not only government, but also the methods of getting elected and reelected. No matter what we may think of politician's ethics, manners, integrities, or personalities, politicians are a very creative group of people. Politicians got our votes, didn't they?

The President and the political staff utilize the *State of the Union Address* to support political positions or policies. One process of this marketing campaign is to invite particular and carefully selected citizens who have experienced living circumstances that can be marketed to reinforce the President's positions or actions on politically charged topics such as welfare, health, economics, technology development, defense, bio-engineering, and other topics. James Madison, one of the producers of the U.S. Constitution and the secretary for the meetings that developed the U.S. Constitution, would be amazed and intrigued at how psychological and commercialized the *Information on the State of the Union* report to Congress has become. It is interesting to consider whether James Madison would use the report to Congress requirement for his political gain and success if he were alive in this world of politics today.

The tone and effect of the speech is usually uplifting, motivating, creates excitement, and spawns hope, vision, and fulfillment of the "American Dream". The speech usually contains a few comments that are skillfully directed as political artillery designed to win the confidence of citizens on controversial topics of legislative, executive, and judicial government issues.

Statistics show that most Americans do not tune in by television or radio to hear the live presentation of the presidential speech. That laziness or indifference by the citizens is in itself the essence of freedom that allows us to choose to not participate in government activities. There are no punishments or penalties for that. No American citizen is forced by the government to listen to the *State of the Union Address*. The apathy and poor citizenship of many registered voters confirms to the politicians that the public is not always responsible or accountable for the workings of government. Politicians detect this voter apathy and seize the opportunity to use the Presidential report to the Congress to slip many powerful concepts and strategies past the unassuming and voters who lack knowledge about the activities and strategies of government.   With fewer listening voters, it is easier to gain government approval of concepts and strategies.   Voter apathy in managing government action is the *mother* of uncontrolled government.   The willingness of politicians to take quiet personal advantage of the voter apathy is the *father* of uncontrolled government.

Many people believe or suspect that the Reagan Administration had placed phenomenal pressures upon NASA to launch the Space Shuttle *Challenger* on time to support the televised address by the President to the Congress and the American people.   Three questions capture the issue.   The answers to these questions will develop from dissecting the DRAFT and DELIVERED versions of the address.

1.   What can be assumed about the purpose and content of the address to the Congress and the nation?

2.   What does the 1986 *State of the Union Address* reveal about the politics of President Reagan's Administration and the Presidential-mandated *Teacher-In-Space Program* at NASA?

3.   Is there evidence that President Reagan and the Republican Party directed political pressures upon NASA to launch Christa McAuliffe into space to support the timing of the 1986 *State of the Union Address?*

The DRAFT version of the speech, dated January 25, 1986, will be assessed. Then, the DELIVERED version of the speech, dated January 28, 1986, will be assessed. The differences between the two versions of the speech should reveal the intent of the speech regarding the political strategies and efforts by the Republican Party elected officials.

The draft speech was obtained from the archivists of the Ronald Reagan Presidential Library in Semi Valley, California in accordance with the Freedom of Information Act (FOIA), Title 5 of the U.S. Public Codes. The draft speech was composed of twelve pages of double spaced text. There is one minor editorial change on page two of the draft speech. The highly refined content and structure of the draft speech indicates that either expert level speech writing for first draft was produced, or expert-level collaboration had occurred between the speech writers and many advisors on economics, international politics, defense, science, exploration, social science and psychology.

As we commence to assess the draft and final versions of the *State of the Union Address*, certain assumptions about the nature and will of American citizens must be base-lined so that the political actions of elected politicians may have purpose and meaning to the citizens who work very hard to survive and to prosper in the American culture. American citizens are heroes of the democratic republic of The United States of America. Americans do not hope and wish for Tragedy and failure upon government actions.

ASSUMPTIONS ABOUT AMERICAN CITIZENS:

1.   Most American citizens love their country, either from patriotism or from the joys and benefits of living in America.
2.   Most Americans are busy raising their families and are faithful and loyal to that natural duty.
3.   American citizens and families have various problems of their own that occupy most of the time of each day. Not much time remains to invest toward running federal or state government. Life is complex and there simply is not enough time in a day to do everything.
4.   Americans elect politicians to run the business of government on their behalf so that the citizen doesn't have to invest time in the details of the responsibility of governing.
5.   Many Americans will never in their life times participate in government activities because those people are not at all interested and will not invest the time or money to participate.
6.   Tragedies within government activities will happen even if all American citizens participate in the government process.
7.   Life in America is far from perfect and the federal government is not the total solution for imperfection.

The first launch countdown of the *Challenger* 51-L mission occurred on January 27, 1986 and was scrubbed and rescheduled for January 28, 1986 due to the problem with the close-out of the Orbiter's side hatch to the Crew Module. The scheduled date of the *State of the Union Address* was a firm date of January 28,

1986. Had the *Challenger's* launch occurred on January 27, that would have meant that *Challenger* would have been in Earth orbit for more than one day when the worldwide broadcast of President Reagan's speech been broadcast. The scrub of the first launch countdown resulted in *Challenger* being launched on January 28, 1986 at 11:28 A.M., approximately nine hours and thirty-two minutes before Reagan's speech was to be broadcast live to the world.

There was a tone of discomfort in many space program workers that developed into a tone of resentment that the third civilian would be given a free ride into space because of their career positions. U.S. Senator Jake Garn (Republican – Utah) and U.S. Representative Bill Nelson (Democrat – Florida) had already flown their free rides into space by using their political and budgetary funding powers over NASA as a persuasion. Who in NASA would say no to the leaders in the legislative branch of government who represent the people when the legislators insist on a free ride into space at NASA's expense?

It is true that on many occasions legislators go for rides in military equipment to see if the citizens are getting what was ordered, but they are legislators, not quality control or performance experts. The Legislative and Executive branches of federal government write and execute the laws to which NASA must dutifully operate. If a legislator wants to go for a Space Shuttle ride, there is not much that rocket scientists and program managers at NASA can lawfully do to override such directives.

NASA's working environment was one of academia, manufacturing, quality control, and extreme flight-testing and applications of new technologies. Education and training were primary investments of the lifestyles of NASA and contractor personnel. Space workers understood the need for training, or schooling. Teachers teach. That also made sense to the space workers. Certainly, the fundamental idea of flying a schoolteacher into space was logical and inevitable. But the timing of flying a schoolteacher into space was wrong and resulted in NASA's awesome historical reputation sounding like a violin severely out of tune and unable to keep time with the rhythm and score of the music. The *Teacher-In-Space* concept did not fit well into the daunting technical and safety realities of the Space Shuttle program at that time, early in the flight experience of the Space Shuttle vehicles.

Before 1986, NASA had already flown two politicians into space. NASA had experienced the trepidations and extra risks inherent with flying civilians who had no obvious link to the purposes and intent of the NASA charter of *Title 42 of the Public Health and Welfare Codes* of public law. Yes, they were politicians with powers and authorities over NASA, but the average citizen who paid for the costs to fly the politicans did not request that the politicians fly. The average citizen did not understand the reasoning for such unnecessary passengers except that politicians are well known for taking care of themselves first, and then their constituents. The pay raises that legislators have voted into law at the midnight hour are evidence of that selfishness and lack of government performance to serve sufficiently. The orbiting legislators were paid thousands of dollars per year more than the Commanders of their flights. Underpaid NASA astronauts performed the safe return and landing of the legislators.

In 1985, NASA was straining under the burdens of many complex technical design and reliability problems of the Space Shuttle systems. The Space Shuttle

Program was developing shortages of critical spare parts to keep the fleet of Space Shuttles flying safely. By 1985, NASA was receiving direct pressures from Congress to increase the Space Shuttle launch rate in an effort to show the Space Shuttle concept could pay for itself as hoped for in many dreams of people who argued to establish and fund the Space Shuttle Program. The NASA organization did not possess the human or financial resources to contend with the periodic "boost-a-politician-to-orbit" antics. The Legislative branch of government that was in official service to the nation during the first half of the decade of the 1980s allowed NASA to be used for the personal advantage and gain of those civilian legislators who flew into space.

Most NASA employees were extremely busy working on Space Shuttle missions to invest much time listening to the news about President Reagan's *Teacher-In-Space Program*. At Kennedy Space Center, our exposure to the politics and progress of that program was limited to gossip, local newspaper articles, and grocery store news rack articles.

Regardless of NASA employee opinions or feelings of the *Teacher-In-Space Program*, this program was conceived and ordered from the top, The White House, The President. NASA has been always faithful to the agency's federal charter contained in the *Title 42 of the Public Health and Welfare Codes* and faithful to the leadership and decisions of the President and Congress. As expected, NASA was dedicated to comply with President Reagan's Executive Order to boost the schoolteacher to Earth orbit.. NASA is accountable to the President and Congress for all orders and charters issued to the agency. Duty, honor, country prevails.

The casual discussions between employees at

Kennedy Space Center consisted of typical comments such as, "If a teacher can fly, why can't I?" Another typical comment was, "How many "Boondogglers" do they plan to fly?" The term "Boondoggler" referred to a person who took unnecessary trips and money in the name of government work. Except for these casual and typical comments, the KSC workers were simply too busy processing Space Shuttles and payloads to spend much time debating the *Teacher-In-Space* issues.

The first draft of *The State of the Union Address* of January 25, 1986, contained thoughts about a strong and growing America, a comparison of the nation in 1986 to a nation that "shut the gates of opportunity, threatening to crush the very roots of our freedom." From the first page of the speech it initiated the build up that what brought America back to common sense was the American people. This first draft speech included the hero segment in which the President would showcase several heroes of the American people.

The speech develops excitement that the "storm clouds loom darkest – right here in Washington, DC", then builds on Congress passing laws "forcing the Federal Government to live within its means." The speech then addresses the new laws passed regarding April 15, the tax deadline in America for paying income earned taxes, "the very day America's families have to foot the bill for the budgets you (Congress) produce." The speech then states, "It's time we reduced the Federal budget and leave the family budget alone." Remember, the American families and citizens are the source for the annual and traditional Reagan hero segment.

The speech discusses national defense, and keeping America strong and free. In 1986, the Soviet

Union was considered by the U.S. government to be the number one threat to U.S. national security. Knocking down barriers to national growth and goals of freer and fairer trade are addressed.   Problems suffered by farmers from unwise government practices, and a Directive to then Secretary of the U.S. Treasury, Jim Baker, to explore a possible international meeting "to discuss the role and relationship of our currencies" were included.

On page seven of the twelve-page speech, the heavy political topics change to a less stressful tone that relates a "renaissance in education with rising Scholastic Aptitude Test (S.A.T.) scores for 3 years." The speech defended a pro-life position that the American Dream is related to "the condition of America's families." The speech describes the welfare system to be failed and in a crisis and that the system is a "sinful waste of human spirit and potential." Easily imagined at this point of the DRAFT speech is the emerging link to President Reagan's American heroes segment that will shine a light of hopeful examples upon the issues that the speech implies are the priorities for America.

Affordable insurance and an instant shift to speaking "directly to America's younger generation – because you hold the destiny of our Nation in your hands." Societal temptations, illegal drug use and abuse, "superhuman feats of self-control" are pointed out and then an instant change of tone that states, "Never has there been a more exciting time to be alive – a time of rousing wonder and heroic achievement. As they said in the film, <u>Back to the Future</u>: "Where we're going, we don't need roads." These lines of page nine of the speech are suggestive of a setup to introduce the American heroes. Physicists, sub-atomic parti-

cles, religious faith, astronomer's use of powerful telescopes to look back into time, "possibly back to the
moment of creation" are all there.

The proposed *Aerospace Plane* is described that will
provide Mach 25 "Low Earth Orbit" flights between
Dulles Airport to Tokyo by the end of the 1990s. Low
Earth Orbit (LEO) is exactly where Christa McAuliffe
would have been on January 28, 1986 if the launch had
been successful on January 27 or January 28. The
speech then defended the Strategic Defense Initiative
Organization (SDIO) "to make our strategic defense
real for the citizens of planet Earth." Arms control
negotiations in Geneva to reduce nuclear weapons
count is stated but continues "But arms control is no
substitute for peace. We know that peace follows in
freedom's path."

There does appear to be a lead up to the
American hero segment, but the speech writer is
hanging out a virtual laundry list of Republican Party
planks, or issues, on the way to the American hero
segment climax.

Page twelve of the speech states, "After all we've
done so far, let no one say this Nation cannot reach the
destiny of our dreams. America believes, America is
ready, America can win the race to the future—and we
shall." These words and thoughts suggest that a higher
force is responsible for our nation's destiny and that
there is a clear vision of hope for the future. The
climax of the speech is within the words, "to venture a
daring enterprise … to discover a new Universe inside
a tiny silicon chip or a single human cell." Then, the
first draft speech had the heroes segment here. After
the heroes were to be introduced, the speech writer
used words, "You are the heroes of our hearts. We
look at you and know it is true – in this land of dreams

fulfilled, where greater dreams may be imagined, nothing is impossible, no victory is beyond our reach, no glory will ever be too great. Now, it is up to us, all of us, to make America ready for that day when our work will pale before the greatness of America's Champions in the 21st Century.

The world's hopes rest with America's future. America's hopes rest with all of you. So let us go forward to create our world of tomorrow – in faith, unity, and love. Thank you. God bless you and God bless America."

Reagan had earned the title of "The Great Communicator." If this speech had been delivered on the wings of a safe and successful launch of *Challenger*, that night could have been President Reagan's finest night as President. Reagan's magical oratorical skills would have combined truth, faith, hope, love, parents, teachers, students, success, and learning about who we are as humans into a convincing case that Christa McAuliffe's dreams were fulfilled by hard work rather than President Reagan's Executive Order of 1985 that established the *Teacher-In-Space Program* at NASA.

With every Space Shuttle launch comes the time when the training and publicity have been completed and it is time to fly. NASA's Showtime is launch day. Reality becomes very personal when the Astronauts complete the ride in the Astro-van to the launch Pad, exit the Astro-van, and look up to see the enormous and massive high-performance rocket in which they are about to fly. Human emotions and nerves remind the Astronauts that the event is real and that the risks and hazards are no joke. Excitement and trepidation about the imminent launch combine to produce emotions of nervousness and feelings of respect for the Space Shuttle design and power. Astronauts and test pilots commonly experience those humbling sights, feelings, and emotions. NASA and contractor employees working in the White Room on the launch Pad, and in the Firing Rooms have witnessed many facial and body expressions of Astronauts that were generated by nervousness and excitement during the launch preparations on the day of launch. Teachers and Test Pilots alike experience the same emotions, they just deal with them differently.

One of my NASA colleagues, Mr. Turner, was the NASA Quality Control person in the Orbiter Access Arm White Room during the 51-L crew ingress who presented Christa McAuliffe a Red Delicious apple as a gesture of respect for her and her profession as an educator. The time of launch is the point when political arguments and program financial debates cease. Liftoff is the proof of which side of the debates won and there is no turning back. Liftoff reveals the degree to which NASA employees have been faithful to the Space Shuttle missions, to the national laws, to the laws of science, and to the political products of the government. We launched the teacher from KSC Complex 39, Pad B, January 28, 1986–as ordered by the President of the United States.

The assessment of the speeches, the tone of the space program employees, and the reality of politics in America are sufficient to show that certainly President Reagan had a clear political agenda. That agenda was to convince teachers to vote for Republicans, regardless of what lobbyists and unions were saying about the performance of Republicans on issues of education in America.

President Reagan appealed to teacher's intense feelings and emotions by offering them a chance to be recognized and rewarded with a flight into space for their worth and value to society. Teachers love their students, are generally underpaid, and take chances and risks every day to teach their students. The President's strategy to gain the confidence and votes of the teachers was creative and gutsy. Teachers naturally respond with enthusiasm and a competitive spirit to ideas and challenges that may produce direct benefits to the learning experience of the students. Almost every teacher in our pre-college school systems is fully committed to educating the children to become responsible, knowledgeable, and wise adults. My teachers were certainly of that lifestyle. Teachers truly love their students and President Reagan definitely incorporated the emotional attachment of teachers to their students to make his political point in the Presidential speech.

Most teachers are living heroes of our society because they continually give and sacrifice time, money, energy, and prayers to the mission of teaching their students. The governments of the world can never value or appreciate contributions by teachers to society any more than do the students who experience the excitement of learning that happens every day.

It is clear that NASA was following the lead that President Reagan and his staff were producing to gain the teachers votes for Republican Party elections at all levels of government. NASA's commitment to duty is the reason the agency followed the Executive Order to conduct the *Teacher-In-Space Program.* NASA was always under pressure by Congress to meet the NASA launch schedule. Congress had relentlessly been pressuring NASA for years to have quicker Space Shuttle launch turnarounds and more launches per year. Even if the Reagan Presidential staff had orchestrated a coincident launch to parallel the *State of the Union Address,* the launch delays from the *Columbia* 61-C launch, combined with the mechanical glitches and weather issues of *Challenger* 51-L launch attempts, it would have appeared more likely that the television production and broadcast of the speech may not have been capable of having Christa McAuliffe speak from Earth orbit. *Challenger* could have still been sitting on launch Pad 39B as President Reagan would have delivered the speech on January 28, 1986.

After having conducted significant research into the question of Presidential pressure to NASA to launch on time, it is my belief that Christa McAuliffe's participation in the "hero segment" of the Reagan speech had to be OPTIONAL. If the speech and the 51-L mission schedules worked well together, Reagan would utilize Christa. If not, Reagan had other heroes who would make the magic of the modern-day speech happen.

The final version of the Presidential speech is "TEXT OF AN ADDRESS BY THE PRESIDENT ON THE STATE OF THE UNION", U.S. Capitol, Washington, DC, January 28, 1986 and this delivered speech version has NO hero segment. This speech was published by The White House, Office of the Press Secretary, and was embargoed for wire transmission until 7:30 P.M. (EST), and authorized for public release at 9:00 P.M. (EST).

It was merely coincidental that the *Challenger* 51-L launch finally occurred on the same day as the originally scheduled date of the *State of the Union Address*. If the 51-L mission been successful, and had the President's speech occurred on the day before *Challenger's* reentry and landing, the speech and the launch date would not have been such a controversial issue. The record-setting delays of the *Columbia* 61-C mission came very close to shifting the *Challenger* 51-L launch into February, 1986. No one at NASA expected so many launch scrubs as happened on the 61-C mission.   Spacing launch schedules for sequential missions is a routine procedure in Space Shuttle planning and scheduling. Launch delays can and do occur.

President Reagan could have used another one of his carefully selected American heroes whether Christa had been in Earth orbit or returned safely to Earth. The fatal crash of *Challenger* ended the possibility of using either scenario and the President's televised speech was postponed.   Prior to President Reagan's *Teacher-In-Space Program* Christa was unknown to the world outside of her community in Concord, New Hampshire. She was a Hero of education and to her students, family, and friends. The *Teacher-In-Space Program* goal was to make the chosen teacher, Christa, a national Hero, manufactured by the authority and powers of the President.

Christa did not need to be part of a government program to serve her students, society, family, or God. Christa, like the other crewmembers of the *Challenger's* last flight, was a good person with a genuine love for country, family, and a passionate career.

Some people feel that President Reagan should have kept his politics out of NASA's work and that the President was responsible for the loss of public trust of NASA and its existence. President Reagan had no hand in the 1975 NASA approval of the flawed design of the Solid Rocket Boosters that caused near crashes of many Space Shuttle flights that culminated with the *Challenger* 51-L crash.   President Reagan and his staff loved America and worked for freedom as much as anyone in the NASA and contractor organizations.

It can be easily argued that President Reagan was allowed to continue virtually unopposed regarding implementation of *The Teacher-In-Space Program* because voters,   citizens,   news   media,   and   government watchdog groups were not aware or understanding of what the Republican Party was doing in 1985 and 1986 to obtain the support and votes of teachers. If the government's plans for education and space exploration were wrong according to the laws and best interest of the people of the United States of America, then those apathetic citizens should have done something legal to stop it. Complaints after the Tragedy cannot be validated for those who did not invest knowledge, wisdom, sweat, and accountability in the first place when the Tragedy could have been reduced by not allowing the teacher to fly on the high performance and risky Space Shuttle.

President Reagan and his staff, in my knowledge from my research, did nothing illegal, nothing immoral. President Reagan only did what any other politician would have done in allowing the administrative staff to do all that is possible to glean power and respect for their party by associating themselves with the supportive and marketable events of the day. The men and women of President Reagan's administration were brokenhearted and grieved because of the loss and pain suffered by the *Challenger* Astronauts. Americans and other people from everywhere on Earth grieved because of the Tragedy. The crash of *Challenger* and the deaths of the Astronauts made all who knew of it sad and reminded everyone how fragile we are as the Human Race. If the crash had not happened, President Reagan, Christa, and NASA would have enjoyed the high position of being heroes for recognizing the value of quality education in our world today. The fatal crash has negated and overwhelmed any suggestion that the Reagan Administration revolutionized or improved education in America. Politics is risky business and the *Teacher-In-Space Program* failed to produce the results that

President Reagan and his staff had hoped. Historically and politically, the *Teacher-In-Space Program* was a disaster for President Reagan. The Republican Party never regained credibility in dealing with the national problems in education that plague the United States into the 21st Century.

President Reagan did not financially support NASA any more than Presidents who have served since President Lyndon B. Johnson. President Reagan was THE supporter of the *Strategic Defense Initiative Organization (SDIO)* and the strengthening of the U.S. military. Many space workers worked for NASA for the same reasons that I worked there. The reasons were because of the peaceful programs of exploration, scientific research and discovery, and the potential of solving the ordinary problems of life on Earth dealing with energy, new materials, and medical treatments. NASA and contractor employees of the 1970 to 1991 period who were for the peaceful exploration and research applications of space vehicles were never adequately supported by the Presidents and Congresses of that period regarding financial and operational aspects of space exploration. Had those Presidents and Congresses adequately supported space exploration, many more space probes would have been in space, NASA would have at least eight Space Shuttle Orbiters, two more Space Shuttle launch Pads, the *Shuttle-C* unmanned launch vehicle, a Mars mission completed, more advanced studies of the Sun, more Earth resources satellites in orbit, and many more astronomy probes.

If President Reagan and his staff could live those exciting years of the 1980s over again, perhaps President Reagan would let space exploration and rocket science problems be worked and solved by

NASA, and require politics and problems of education to be worked by the people who know best about how to construct, organize, and operate education: the local educators, parents, and students.   President Reagan made this point in the *State of The Union Address* that was finally delivered to the nation.   He said, "It wasn't Government and Washington lobbies that turned education around – it was the American people who, in reaching for excellence, knew to reach back-to-basics."

The history of the 1980s would have been very different if NASA had been left out of the politics of the teaching and political industries.   NASA's Charter under *Title 42 of the Public Health and Welfare Codes* does not outline NASA's political responsibilities.   The Charter mostly authorizes that the agency conduct scientific research in the atmosphere and space, build and fly rockets, develop ground transportation systems, research energy, and share far and wide what is learned. Political strategies are thrown onto NASA by politicians who take advantage of the U.S. Constitutional provisions of *Article I, Section 8*, that has been the basis of the authority for politicians to make the mountain of "additional laws" that our society is swamped with today. The debates over such additional laws have included the debates of how to design and operate the education systems of America.   The many lessons learned from the *Challenger* Tragedy make us learn once again how responsible and accountable we are, individually and collectively, as authors and actors of our own history and legacy to the future.

CHAPTER 17

THE INVESTIGATION ENDS

By the end of the spring of 1986, the *Challenger* Tragedy investigation team had compiled tremendous amounts of evidence, documentation, photographs, lab analysis, and interview results. Virtually every cubic foot of the facilities that are used to process the Space Shuttle for launch and landing had been scrutinized as suspect contributors to the catastrophe. Procedures, processes, flight and ground hardware, organizational issues, launch decision rules, communications between space centers and customers, potential sabotage and fraud, and public comments were all analyzed by the *Rogers Presidential Commission*. NASA had a complete an honest investigation that was unprecedented even by NASA standards.

Every procedure for ground and flight processing, launch, and landing has since been progressively reviewed and corrected where necessary. Some of those changes were technical; some changes were semantic for understanding the intent and meaning of the text. Signatures of engineers, managers, and quality personnel involved with the writing, review, and the working of those hundreds of procedures were analyzed for legibility. Because some signatures could not be read clearly, the *Rogers Presidential Commission* recommended that all signatures on procedures be printed, then signed in cursive writing, and rubber-stamped if necessary for accountability.

With the Space Shuttle wreckage hands-on work very close to completion, I was beginning to receive calls and requests to support other aspects of the *Challenger* investigation that were progressing throughout KSC. Those investigation detailed reviews in other locations at KSC were evidence to me that the NASA team was still alive and well in the ranks of employees. The atmosphere at KSC was noticeably quiet since so many contractor personnel had been laid off. It seemed as if those workers had been on holiday. So many offices at the space center had no employees.

The investigation team made the transition to cleaning up the Logistics Facility because of the mess we had made with all the Space Shuttle wreckage. The cleaning activities were very therapeutic for us psychologically. We could now begin to think of normal routines and having the time to be part of family and friends again like we all lived the year before in 1985.

Ron Phelps called for our final reports, photographs, videotapes, and notes to be submitted for the official record of our work. The *Rogers Presidential Report on the Challenger Accident* was being compiled and edited as our final reports were being submitted. A great amount of work had been done to produce the Presidential Report. Had the report been late, the historic actions of President Ronald Reagan and Congress to continue funding and support of manned space flight and to replace the *Challenger* with the new Orbiter, *Endeavour*, may have been missed.

Astronaut Bob Crippen had briefed the investigation team that NASA had approved a limited number of *Challenger* wreckage items to be salvaged and used in engineering research projects that would commence immediately at various NASA centers. One of the wreckage items was a main landing gear that was in amazingly good condition after having fallen as part of the left wing to the Earth from about 43,500 feet. That landing gear was used at NASA Langley in Virginia to evaluate wheel and brake capabilities. It was mounted to the large, outdoor water-powered sled for testing to simulate Orbiter landing touchdown dynamic loads.

There we were, nearly halfway through a year that had begun so tragically for so many people. I wondered many times how long it would be before we would fly Space Shuttles again. I knew that the SRB engineers and manufacturers would be incredibly busy.

I knew that it would be a long time before we would hear the sounds of SRBs thundering through the Florida skies shaking the Earth and buildings. For the next few years, we had to leave such sounds to be made only by the Florida thunderstorms.

The *Rogers Presidential Commission* had one more task to accomplish before disbanding. A complete report had to be submitted to President Ronald Reagan that included the collected data, interviews with space workers and managers, photographs and film, analysis, public testimonies, lab analysis reports, and most importantly, *Recommendations to the President*.

RECOMMENDATIONS TO PRESIDENT RONALD REAGAN

FROM THE *CHALLENGER* ACCIDENT PRESIDENTIAL COMMISSION

REGARDING THE FUTURE OF NASA

[Recommendations in response and in conclusion to Presidential Executive Order, 12546, dated February 3, 1986, which established the Presidential Commission on the Space Shuttle *Challenger* Accident.]

1. Redesign the Shuttle Solid Rocket Boosters (SRBs) with National Research Council oversight.

2. Rework the Shuttle Program management structure, include Astronauts in the management process, and create a Shuttle Safety Panel.

3. Conduct a review of Shuttle design Criticality Review and Hazard Analysis.

4. Create a Safety Reliability & Quality Assurance office to report directly to the NASA Administrator.

5. Improve communications throughout NASA.

6. Improve Shuttle landing safety covering vehicle, runway, and other issues.

7. Study and solve launch abort and crew escape options.

8. Produce a Shuttle flight rate consistent with NASA's resources.

9. Develop maintenance safeguards for Criticality I components. Criticality I items are those that, if they fail, the results are the loss of the crew, the vehicle, and the payload. This proposal aimed for methods to analyze and report problems so that safety concerns do not get lost in the schedule, and for a tailored inspection program for flight and ground hardware and software.

THE PRESIDENTIAL COMMISSION'S CONCLUDING THOUGHTS:

"The Commission urges that NASA continue to receive the support of the Administration and the nation. The agency constitutes a national resource that plays a critical role in space exploration and development. It also provides a symbol of national pride and technological leadership.

The Commission applauds NASA's spectacular achievements of past and anticipates impressive achievements to come. The findings and recommendations presented in this report are intended to contribute to future NASA successes that the nation both expects and requires as the 21st Century approaches."

(Source: The Presidential Commission on the Space Shuttle *Challenger* Accident Report, June 6, 1986)

Clearly, the *Challenger* crash investigation concluded that NASA's work has phenomenally high risks and hazards and that the investigators, President Reagan, and U.S. Congress were willing to continue to invest the money, time, and labor to allow NASA to continue to develop and employ technologies in advancing the exploration of the Universe. The findings and recommendations of the investigation team combined with the leadership and decision of the President and Congress demonstrated how grace, forgiveness, and second chances are afforded to teams that genuinely strive to follow meaningful rules and procedures. As Astronaut Gus Grissom stated, "Do good work." I say, *"Second chances are afforded to those who consistently do good work."*

The taxpayers are very generous and financially supportive to government organizations that are led by managers who instinctively know how to revise rules and procedures that are defeating the agency's mission. Taxpayers want lower tax burdens and they are smart and wise enough to know that it takes money to operate government functions. Taxpayers deserve a dollar's worth of product for a dollar of tax money. The stewards of the system must be held accountable for this performance.

CHAPTER 18

"RETURN TO FLIGHT," STS-26

Several months had passed since that historic and horrific day of the crash of *Challenger*. The NASA and contractor team and most people on Earth had grieved for the Astronauts and had become familiar with the Space Shuttle and NASA culture. The American people had realized more than ever that space flight is complicated and dangerous. Prior to the Tragedy, many people indicated their extemporaneous willingness to fly aboard the Space Shuttle by saying, "If NASA would let me, I would go." After the Tragedy, as a nervous joke of their fear of flying aboard a Space Shuttle, some of those same people said "I won't go if she's gonna blow." The threatening design complexities and hazards of the Space Shuttle rapidly separated the daredevils from the carnival riders.

STS-26 would be the first Space Shuttle mission after 51-L and would be flown using the Space Shuttle *Discovery*. All of NASA was committed to flying the perfect mission, with the perfect crew, and to regain the public's confidence that not only was NASA capable of the great performances in space, but that space flight was necessary and worth the investment. The STS-26, Orbiter *Discovery*, "Return To Flight" mission was comparatively as significant as Astronaut Alan Shepard's sub-orbital flight into space aboard *Freedom* 7, the *Mercury* spacecraft that was flown atop the *Redstone* rocket in 1961. The comparative similarity was that NASA had to prove its procedures, hardware, people, and integrity all over again. It was as if NASA's history of successful space flights had never existed.

Commander Rick Hauck was selected as the STS-26 Mission Commander. Hauck was a veteran of several Space Shuttle missions before STS-26 and that helped make him a great choice for this all-important Shuttle flight. He was a polite man and a pilot who operated with sound logic and an educated seriousness as a Shuttle Commander, just what NASA needed at that time. Many Astronauts could have done the job well, but Hauck was a great choice.

I drove through the KSC Gate 2 on Merritt Island on my way to the STS-26 Space Shuttle Rollout-to-the-Pad ceremony at Complex 39. The KSC guard at the gate stopped me and asked me to pull forward and let the *ABC News* reporter Betina Gregory ask me a question about my feelings of the STS-26 Space Shuttle *Discovery's* rollout from the VAB to the launch Pad.

In some words I said to her that I hope that the public realizes that NASA's efforts strive to accomplish the most yield with the resources allocated to the agency to accomplish the missions. I encourage the public to be perceptive of NASA for the future, and to take the risks with the agency. The NASA legacy has been a risk since the first thought about flying monstrous liquid-fueled rockets, missions to the Moon, Mars, and the stars. Many of the great ideas and dreams of NASA were never brought into reality because people have allowed politics, money, and fear to steal their dreams. The proposed unmanned Heavy Lift Space Shuttle, *Shuttle C (C is for Cargo)*, is an example of a NASA program that was cancelled by the senseless funding arguments over *Title 42 of the Public Health and Welfare Codes* money. The cancellation in 1990 of *Shuttle C* paralyzed NASA's growth for efficient, safe, and cost-effective boosting of heavy and large volume cargo to Low Earth Orbit for missions such as construction and service of the *International Space Station*, or for future missions to the outer planets of our Solar System. The cancellation of the *Shuttle C* Program and other rocket programs such as the *Heavy Lift Vehicle, HLV*, were your losses as a taxpayer. NASA was forced to use the Space Shuttle over dozens of flight to do what *Shuttle C* or what *HLV* could have done in a few less costly heavy-lift launches to Earth orbit.

Unmanned launch vehicles are bargains of expense compared to manned launches that are the most costly. All of the Space Shuttle launches that transport sections of the *International Space Station* to Low Earth Orbit could have been launches to fly payloads for paying customers from private industry. Those paying customers would have significantly reduced the operating costs of the Space Shuttle Program, but instead, the taxpayers have paid for the dozens of flights that are necessary to construct the space station. The money that has been spent for those space station construction Shuttle flights could have paid for many *Shuttle C* or *HLV* vehicles and greatly expanded the launch readiness and payload-to-orbit capacity of NASA. NASA did not fully utilize "The NASA Method" in planning for *Shuttle C* and *HLV* programs.

The employees of KSC gave their best efforts to ensure that the *Challenger* flight of 51-L would be an isolated Tragedy, not to be repeated in any way on *Discovery's* upcoming flight. The STS-26 mission had to be successful. A "commitment to good work" signature book was produced by NASA Operations and Public Affairs and was routed to be autographed by all KSC employees who had worked on STS-26. The book was presented to the STS-26 Astronauts on July 4, 1988. NASA orchestrated a wonderful and patriotic ceremony that night under the Xenon floodlights on the east side of the VAB during the STS-26 rollout to the Pad for the Shuttle *Discovery*. The rollout of *Discovery* from the Vehicle Assembly Building (VAB) to the launch Pad was extremely emotional and the excitement and joy was reminiscent of the 1980 rollout to Pad A of *Columbia*, STS-1.

Many lights, news reporters, and guests regenerated the kinds of feelings we experienced in the good old days of early Space Shuttle flights. The rollout of *Discovery* was highlighted by the presentation of the employees' autograph book to Commander Hauck and his crew so that the crew would fly the book aboard *Discovery* during the STS-26 Mission. The book was to be returned to KSC after a safe landing so that visitors to KSC could share and appreciate it. It was on display several years at Spaceport USA at KSC and is NASA's way of sharing the commitment of the space workers to quality, education, and ethics in engineering that builds the public's trust.

The STS-26 launch of *Discovery* was the conclusion of a very long and tiring episode of aerospace history. The period of time between the *Columbia* launch of Mission 61-C in January of 1986, and the launch of *Discovery* STS-26 on September 29, 1988, was a tedious and exhausting experience of building a better NASA and showing the world that America wasn't going to quit. The spirit of NASA had become humbled and certainly different. The leadership of NASA was composed of all new people who knew that safe flight was Job-One. The entire NASA process of planning, designing, building, testing, and reporting procedures had been overhauled. NASA was confident that all of the critical safety-of-flight issues had been addressed and solved by the *Challenger* investigation.

However, there was one Space Shuttle Orbiter

design deficiency that had not been solved. The drag parachute that was to help slow the speed of the Orbiter during landing rollout had not been added to the Orbiter configuration. The Orbiters continued flying and landing for another four years with brakes on the Main Landing Gear (MLG) that could provide slightly less than half of the braking force needed to safely stop the Orbiter. The Orbiter's original brake disk assembly was good for only one landing brake application because of excessive wear and damage from mechanical and thermal stresses that exceeded the design limits of the brake and wheel. After every landing rollout, we had to jack the Orbiter on the runway and remove the brakes for inspection. We were not allowed to tow the Orbiter with the worn and damaged brakes. This was to avoid inducing damage to the brakes that was not caused from their designed application of landing, rollout, and stopping.

NASA continued to take that unnecessary risk with the underpowered brake system for the same reason that resulted in the crash of *Challenger*. NASA management allowed tight schedules and limitations of funding from Congress to result in the continued flying without the mandatory landing drag chute. NASA was lucky that a Return to Landing Site Abort (RTLS) landing with a heavy payload did not occur on flights STS-26 through STS-47 in September 1992. The first operational use of the Orbiter drag chute was on STS-47, September 1992.

It was refreshing to work hard again on the preparations for Space Shuttle Countdown. Once again, we felt that we were doing something worthy of public recognition. We understood that the public owned the Space Shuttle and we were entrusted with the well-being and success of the Space Shuttle, the

Mission, and the Astronauts. It was exhilarating to be doing again what we knew we did best. We had lost so much time of our lives with the investigation, and were thrilled to be back in the rocket and exploration business.

We had been drilled and tested in countdown rehearsal training and the new National Space Transportation System Office (NSTS) members were present in the firing room for the countdown. Astronaut Bob Crippen was the leader of the NSTS office. The group of thirteen provided oversight of the launch countdown and ensured that Astronaut safety concerns, launch procedure inputs, and launch count-down decisions included the Astronauts strapped on their backs atop the rocket at the Pad. The NSTS office was one of the changes that NASA made to ensure the highest level of safety for each Space Shuttle flight.

NSTS Director Bob Crippen had said to many NASA people and to reporters, "If there is a cloud in the sky, we will not launch." As history now shows, the *Discovery* flew through some clouds as she ascended into the Florida skies for STS-26. Dr. Feynman continues to be correct in that human beings do take risks, slight risks though they may seem at the time.

The atmosphere in the Firing Room during the STS-26 countdown was one of professionalism, exact-ness, not getting ahead of the procedure, and the desire to do our best work ever. Each engineer, team leader, quality inspector, and the NSTS team was focused intensely on their responsibilities. Not since STS-1 had there been a more professional team of space explorers making yet another historic voyage.

At T-20 minutes, there was the built-in hold in the countdown. The Launch Director always calls for the countdown clock to stop at exactly the T-20 minute mark to allow the launch team to get caught up on any procedural steps that could have gotten behind during the countdown. NASA had been at this point in the count before, but on this day the launch team was praying for a smooth hold and transition when the countdown resumed.

The NASA Test Director announced, "We will pick up the count at the T-20 minute mark. On my mark— three, two, one, MARK. The countdown clock is counting. " The sounds of those words were music to our ears. All of the sweat, toil, and tears of the past couple of years were now being tested. The adrenaline was flowing in our bodies and the Firing Room was becoming electrified with excitement for the impending launch.

The countdown clock was held one more time at the T-9 minute point in the count. This was a normal ten-minute hold. The one thing that always makes the launch team nervous about this hold in the count is that when the count is resumed, a transition of computer control occurs so that the Ground Launch Sequencer (GLS) computer program can initiate and perform the thousands of lines of computer code necessary to proceed to the T-31 second point in the countdown. The NASA Test Director announced the end of the T-9 minute hold and the start of a new reality for NASA. That reality was one of a perfect countdown and many hopes for a perfect flight into Earth orbit.

The countdown clock continued to tick. The Auxiliary Power Units (APUs) that supply hydraulic pressure to the Orbiter flight controls and landing gear were pre-started at the T-5 minute mark. The Space Shuttle *Discovery* was mechanically, electrically, and pneumatically alive and ready for launch. The spectators outside at the Kennedy Space Center's Complex 39 were on their feet to get the best view of the launch. The people who really owned the Space Shuttle *Discovery*—the Americans who were present at KSC or listening to broadcasts of the countdown—were about to witness the historic launch of the Return To Flight of the Space Shuttle. The countdown was approaching the T-31 second point.

The T-31 second mark was a critical second to a successful countdown in that the GLS program transitions, or gives primary control of the countdown, to the Space Shuttle's onboard computer flight software programs. That transition function causes the launch team to hold their breaths, hoping for success. This time, the T-31 second transition was successful like NASA clockwork. A loud applause and some whistling from the launch team was heard in the Firing Room. The adrenaline was really flowing now, but everyone was focused on their procedures and their computer console monitors. Not one problem could be overlooked. This was NASA's redemption launch and it had to be perfect.

The technological development of the onboard computer control of countdown is a tremendous accomplishment of NASA and computer companies like IBM. Because of this computer system, the launch team could focus on particular critical events for our specific subsystems during the last thirty-one seconds of countdown. The launch team doesn't just sit and watch the computers perform the countdown. Because of the computer's control of the countdown procedure, the engineers in the Firing Rooms can monitor specific parameters that are most important for their system and for ensuring a safe countdown.

Finally, after two years of heartache, sacrifice, and hard work, we heard the voice of NASA's Public

Information Office say the words, "five, four, three, two, one, and liftoff!" After a few seconds, the thunderous shock wave of noise from the Shuttle's three powerful hydrogen engines and the two SRBs rocked the Launch Control Complex. It had been a long time since we had felt such exhilaration. The bright massive flames from the SRBs had never looked better as they painted the skies above Florida's Space Coast, over the Atlantic Ocean, and into the darkness of space.

The commander, Rick Hauck, called the flight trajectory performance cues during flight. As the *Discovery* cleared the launch tower, Commander Hauck called, "Roll Program." About one minute later into flight Hauck called, "GO at throttle-up." That call was very emotional for all of us at NASA because that was the last call that Commander Scobee made just moments before the *Challenger* broke apart during the 51-L launch. Everyone on the launch team was relieved to be beyond that call. We felt as if some dark cloud had been removed from over our heads.

The *Discovery* continued to thunder toward its predetermined place and time in space for orbit insertion. The SRBs were jettisoned at about two minutes and twenty seconds into flight. A second time, jubilant applause, cheering, and whistling erupted in the Firing Room as Major Mode 101, the first stage, or main stage as we called it, was complete and successful with the redesigned SRBs. The External Tank performed perfectly once again and was safely jettisoned at about nine minutes into flight. The External Tank engineers, manufacturer, technicians, and quality inspectors have always done remarkable precision work and for the STS-26 Return To Flight launch, those workers did not disappoint anyone.

Challenger's Commander, Dick Scobee, and his crew for the 51-L Mission were certainly in our thoughts that day when we witnessed the successful boost into orbit of *Discovery* and another crew of Astronauts. The STS-26 Mission placed into the Earth orbit the Tracking & Data Relay Satellite (TDRS). It was identical to the TDRS that was destroyed in the *Challenger* crash. The TDRS network of satellites now provides continuous service to Space Shuttles and other spacecraft for communications and data transmission. The successful mission of STS-26 concluded with the *Discovery* free-flying in a controlled descent to the runway. If you have never seen a Shuttle landing in person, I would highly recommend it. Looking up from the ground at the Orbiter passing overhead, the belly of the Orbiter appears chalk-white on the surface of the black tiles due to the thermal radiation emitted from the massive heat load that has been acquired from the dynamic reentry into the Earth's atmosphere. The controlled turns that aligned the *Discovery* with the runway for pre-flair, flair, and touchdown maneuvers were spectacular. The deployment of the landing gear, touchdown, and rollout until wheels stopped was the heroic end of a very tough journey to redeem NASA's reputation.

The Space Shuttle *Discovery* and the STS-26 Astronauts accomplished more than what was called for on the Flight Manifest. That safe and successful flight of STS-26 was the healing ointment on the wounds of NASA, and the fulfillment of so many prayers.

CHAPTER 19

MEMORIES OF THE ASTRONAUTS

The *Challenger's* Astronauts developed many quality relationships with so many of us who were employed by NASA and the contractors for the Space Shuttle Program. The *Challenger* Astronauts were relationship builders. Their generosity, in part, was how they became Astronauts and remained so. The Astronaut selection process and follow-on work is extremely competitive and tiring. An Astronaut must be willing to accommodate everyone involved. An Astronaut who cannot deal with that lifestyle would not blend naturally with the other Astronauts, engineers, and operations managers.

The *Challenger* crew was a likable group of people from diverse backgrounds. Did they have problems? Sure. Did they get tired and frustrated? Did they want to quit and give up sometimes? Possibly. But when they were feeling depressed or defeated, they knew that they could come to any one of us in NASA and things would get better. Sometimes, the best treatment for Astronaut stress was to beat the "hooey" out of a racket ball for an hour or so. Whatever seemed to be the best treatment for the problem is what we did.

My work with the *Challenger* Astronauts was a pleasure and my distinct privilege to live in a time and place that meant so much to all of us. "A chance at bat" is what most of us hope for in our lives. I am sure that all of the people who have been chosen as Astronauts were inspired by people who were unique and made positive impressions upon their lives. The *Challenger*

Astronauts had their heroes, and one of the *Challenger* Astronauts was one of my heroes, Commander Dick Scobee. "Scobes" was an excellent listener and a leader housed inside an unassuming exterior.

A wonderful memory that I have about Dick Scobee occurred in the 1980s when I was a Structures and Mechanisms Systems engineer at Kennedy Space Center and we were just a few days away from the rollout of the Orbiter from the Orbiter Processing Facility (OPF) for the 41-C Mission. The 41-C Mission Astronauts traveled to KSC to thank the OPF technicians, quality inspectors, operations, and engineers for the hard work involved with preparing the Orbiter for flight. That was Scobee's first flight as pilot (co-pilot in the right seat) on the *Challenger* 41-C Mission, April 6, 1984.

The small, two-story annex building that was part of the original OPF office building was where one of my desks was located. I was doing some engineering work in preparation for the structural attachment of the Orbiter to the External Fuel Tank that was about to happen for that Mission after OPF rollout. The Shuttle Mission 41-C Astronauts came into our office where several of us engineers were located. There was Bob Ketterer, *Apollo* Program engineer and Lead Engineer for the Shuttle Thermal Protection System. John Fraley, a former *Apollo* Program Lunar Module structures engineer and Orbiter and facility structures engineer was there. The Astronauts seemed relaxed but determined to speak to everyone. The Astronauts sat with us for about forty minutes and talked about many things. I had the feeling that if I blended into that bunch of Astronauts, maybe I could ride the rocket with them.

I reminded Scobee that I had filled out my application for the Mission Specialist Astronaut job for the Space Shuttle Program. I also told him that there was no point in sending the application to Johnson Space Center because as an employee of NASA, the Astronaut Office would eliminate my application. Back then, the military and the public domain were the only sources allowed for Astronaut candidates. Scobee said, "If you don't send in your application, you know that you will never be selected. So, send it in."

Scobes could see the desire in my eyes. He had encouraged many young and old military personnel before I got to know him, and that is a great part of his legacy. He had worked his own way up to become an Astronaut after having been an enlisted airman.

After that wonderful hour with those Astronauts who were about to carve out another chapter of history in space science and aviation, they had to go. It was difficult to re-focus upon the engineering work after the Crew left. About five minutes later, long after the Astronauts had left the second floor and walked downstairs, someone walked briskly up to my desk from behind and touched me on my right shoulder. It was Scobes. He said again, as if to ensure my actions, "Randy, be sure to submit the application." I will always remember Scobes for walking all the way back upstairs, away from the other Astronauts, to encourage me one last time.

I was in Washington, DC in August, 2000, and visited the graves of the *Challenger* Commander and Pilot at Arlington National Cemetery. It seemed so odd that I was still living and dealing with the newest technologies of electrical avionics design and flight test, and Dick Scobee and Mike Smith had been dead for nearly fourteen years. In 1986, Scobee and Smith were leading the way for the technologies of that day to be ushered into reality by the Mission of *Challenger* 51-L. I had survived all of the many dangerous events that we shared in building, testing, launching, and recovering the new technology Space Shuttles.

As I walked up the hilly streets of Arlington National Cemetary, the many graves made me feel as if I were walking in some sort of dream about people from the past who had loved their country. I was not familiar with most of the names on the graves that I passed, but I wondered what their lives had been like. I continued my promenade to the cemetery section where Scobes was buried. I expected to see an obvious grave marker that could be identified as an Astronaut's grave. I searched all over that section. I walked on grass that I'm not sure that I was allowed to walk upon, trying to find Scobee's grave. I searched back over the route that I had just walked. I saw no one who could help me find it.

I walked back toward the *Tomb of The Unknown Soldiers* to ask about the location of Scobee's grave. Along my way, I noticed an above-ground memorial for some people whom I did not recognize immediately. The memorial included a brass plaque that had the likeness of the *Challenger* Astronauts' faces, although not very recognizable or accurate. I could hardly recognize the images as the Astronauts with whom I had worked. The graves of the Astronauts were not at that memorial site. The search for Scobee's grave was becoming aggravating. I noticed a group of visitors who were sitting aboard a tram that had stopped at the *Tomb of The Unknown Soldiers*. I walked over to the tram bus and asked the driver, "Do you know where the grave of Astronaut F. R. "Dick" Scobee is located? You know, the Commander of the Space Shuttle *Challenger*." The driver said, "His grave is right over there." He was pointing to the memorial for the *Challenger* Astronaut.   I said, "I have already looked over there and I could not find the grave."   He said, "The grave is just to the left of the memorial."

I walked back to the memorial.   The grave was about thirty feet to my left as I faced the monument. The grave marker was plain and looked like the average military marker in Arlington Cemetery.   My knowledge of what Scobes had accomplished and shared in his life caused me to expect a more lavish grave marker.   However, the simple marker was much like the personality of Scobees as I knew him.   It was not like an advertisement, but a low-key and reverent acknowledgement of the resting place for the body of a military person.   It was the resting place of a man who served his country and his public with distinction and with the ultimate sacrifice – his life.   Major Scobee's grave marker is the same size and appearance as one for a military service person who served the rank of private.

I went to work at NASA to build and fly rockets and to explore the Universe.   I did all of that and developed friendships that I will treasure all of my life. Space Shuttle Commander F. R. "Dick" Scobee was one of those friends.   He was a regular man who earned the respect and admiration from those of us who had the opportunity to work with him.

If you care to visit the gravesites of Dick Scobee and Mike Smith at Arlington National Cemetery, this information will assist you after you arrive:

F. R. "DICK" SCOBEE
COMMANDER, SPACE SHUTTLE CHALLENGER

Grave 1129-4, Section 46

Located west of the Tomb of the Unknown Soldiers near Memorial Drive, just left of the *Challenger* Astronaut Memorial

Arlington National Cemetery

MICHAEL JOHN SMITH
PILOT OF SPACE SHUTTLE CHALLENGER

Grave 208-1, Section 7A

Located east and just below the Tomb of the Unknown Soldiers near Roosevelt Drive

Arlington National Cemetery

CHAPTER 20

LIFE GOES ON

The *Challenger* Tragedy of 1986 positioned NASA and its contractors in circumstances of emotional and corporate stresses.   After the chaotic wreckage of *Challenger* plummeted into the Atlantic Ocean, many Americans and space exploration partners of NASA around the world were occupied with thoughts of concerns for NASA's well-being, suspicions of cover-up of information regarding the crash, skepticism about the worth and safety of manned spaceflight, and the passing of innocence about the hazards of launching rockets into space.   A wedge of distrust between the public and NASA developed when the public learned that the SRB segment joints had not been properly designed and that some NASA and contractor engineering managers had concealed the SRB design flaws, and pretended that the safety of flight hazards did not exist.

The *Challenger* crash and deaths of the Astronauts constituted the first Tragedy of the Space Shuttle Program.   The public's sensation of distrust of NASA regarding full disclosure of the crash investigation findings had combined with the disappointment from NASA's poor performance to produce the second Tragedy.

The public had become extensively apathetic regarding the worth, value, purpose, and need for a viable NASA program.   In the months prior to the *Challenger* 51-L launch, that apathy had escalated to a level never seen by this country before (and that includes the apathy by the public that prevailed through the mid-1970s at the end of the *Apollo* Program). The attendance of spectators and guests at the 51-L Mission launch was very sparse.

The *first* of those two Tragedies is one that can be healed in a reasonably short period of time. The new Orbiter, *Endeavour*, replaced Space Shuttle *Challenger* at a cost of five billion dollars to the American taxpayer. The *Challenger* 51-L Astronauts have been laid to rest. The families of the Astronauts have succeeded in making the best of their lives, although they will never forget those they knew as mom, dad, son, daughter, husband, or wife. The families of the Astronauts had to continue living for the future. Those survivors have gone through great efforts to recover their lives.

The *second* Tragedy of the Shuttle Program is immeasurably more intricate to overcome. The public's emotional distrust and disappointment involves many private citizens who have diverse ideas and back-grounds. It was only natural that the public developed a distrust and disappointment of NASA and its engi-neering and service contractors. The public can form opinions in their sleep, based upon limited and sketchy information, reported to them by people who may not even know the truth. NASA can only regain the public's trust and confidence by providing evidence and proof of crash investigation findings, and simulta-neously revitalizing the leadership of the agency.

Affirming the old relationship of public/govern-ment trust was not desirable or realistic after the *Challenger* Tragedy because the public and NASA would not tolerate a repeat of the felonious breach that had occurred with the NASA rocket engineering and launching processes. In conjunction with rebuilding the relationship, NASA was expected to surpass its own historical achievements of performance to restore and ensure the agency's success. NASA had to demonstrate all over again that the agency could manage the Space Shuttle Program at a higher level of safety. NASA had to show to the people of the world that the agency could solve the Space Shuttle design problems, rally the rocket engineers and technicians to do their best quality work ever, and put into operation the technical expertise that is compulsory in the dangerous business of exploring the Universe. The public, U.S. President Reagan, and the U.S. Congress insisted upon an achievable but rigorous recovery plan that would be developed by NASA, the NTSB, and the *Rogers Presidential Commission*. Failure to continue space exploration and research would have been contrary to the American spirit and to the human character.

As this chapter was being written, the United States Congress was debating and preparing to vote for or against the privatization of NASA and the Space Shuttle Program. The goal of Congress was merely to reduce the amount of money that would be allotted for NASA in the federal budget. The change that resulted was that the NASA Civil Service employees were laid off, retired, and a few were reassigned to less critical jobs at NASA. The Space Shuttle Program contractors made their work force lean in numbers and labored to fly the scheduled Shuttle Flight Manifests.

In the summer of 1995, Congress concluded that NASA employees should be involved with the scientific research and development, rather than launching more Space Shuttles. NASA employees should be very involved with research and development of space, aerospace, and Earth resources technologies and their applications. However, Congress failed to tell the public that there were only a few specific plans, or even broad-scoped plans, approved and funded for NASA to manage. This state of affairs for NASA is pitiful. With few NASA programs for Civil Service workers to manage, NASA is not prepared to keep the skilled labor or to direct the wonderful team of engineers and scientists into research and development areas. So, the nation loses its rocket scientists to save a few dollars and we lose great workers who possess extraordinary talents and skills. The corporate knowledge is repeatedly thrown out of the agency and the entire nation suffers.   Contractors are often expected to play both the role of contractor and of Civil Service representatives.   No one believes that a fox makes a reliable guard for the hens in the hen house. Contractors are paid to do one job, not two.

To compound the program management efficiency problems of NASA, *Title 42 of the Public Health and Welfare Codes* has been expanded to include ground transportation development and energy research. NASA cannot solve all problems of science while the workforce is being reduced and funding is being restricted.

Meanwhile, incompetence prevails to unprecedented levels in many federal agencies with many of those incompetent employees being rewarded, promoted, and retained. Competent NASA employees are put out to pasture by employee downsizing programs that do not retain the priceless corporate knowledge.   Many NASA employees are National Resources and should be allowed to contribute to NASA exploration programs. At the same time, government agencies continue to retain incompetent employees who have negative effects in those government services offices. This two-faced and backward practice of managing federal agencies, which is in itself incompetent, is destructive to the written requirements of federal employee performance and recognition. This tragic Congressional and Presidential mismanagement of NASA is softly and rapidly dismantling our technological infrastructures. Our competitors in space exploration are pleased to see the mismanagement of NASA. Congress usually attempts to redistribute the funds in the federal budget and NASA is typically one of the many sacrificial agencies at risk of losing funding.

I am highly concerned that many young people who have graduated from the Space Camps will have few NASA programs to work with as a Civil Service worker, or even as a contractor. From this vantage point it appears that NASA management, the U.S. Congress, and the U.S. Presidents have rested upon a plateau of contentment and have acquired leadership atrophy regarding space programs. It remains to be seen how the current and future U.S. Presidents will direct and lead NASA and the program assignments to the agency. New vision and leadership is needed to solve these problems and to inspire people of the world. Which political party will lead the way?

The fading end of The Golden Age of Space Exploration (1900-2001) may hopefully be grappled and resuscitated by the next generation of eager, bright, young minds who are natural explorers. Or is it sadly possible that my generation and the generation before mine are the only generations that will have conducted the greater portion of the innocent, curious, and awe-inspiring exploration of the heavens and Earth? I certainly hope it is not the case that space exploration is waning. Mankind has merely blown the dust off of the treasure chest called the Universe. Infinity is the amount of time required to observe and learn about everything in the seemingly endless Universe.

The political mood and actions of Congress during 1995 largely ignored NASA's Congressional Charter and showed a reluctance to fund NASA adequately for safe and creative programs and missions. Faster and cheaper is not always a wise methodology for programs of high risks and hazards. This poor attitude of Congress and the President regarding NASA's mission and funding was coincident with the United States' economic health and prosperity setting world records in economic performance whether they were real or imaginary in all categories. Does it take international scares and economic disasters to energize a national space program? Or, do these data and the history of Congress indicate that it is now time to totally privatize the space programs and forget the national flags? Is that the message that Congress is sending to the American people and entrepreneurs from around the world?

I challenge future generations to explore the Universe with an intensity and fervor that will make my generation proud. Rocket science, math, physics, chemistry, biology, and risking your life are not easy courses. That is why the space exploration accomplishments of humans during the 20th Century were so awe-inspiring, magical, mysterious, and supernatural to us as we lived through those historical moments of humanity. Those NASA spectaculars were personal for each of us around the world who witnessed the events. The experience was "all-emotions saturated" as we watched the first flights of *Mercury, Gemini, Apollo,* and the *Space Shuttle.* We vividly remember *Apollo* 8 that took Mankind around the Moon first, and most of all - *Apollo* 11, the first landing of Mankind on the Moon. Some watched by television, some listened by radio, and the fortunate and persistent were live witnesses at the launches.

I was there at Kennedy Space Center to witness the launches of *Apollo* 11, 14, and 17. I worked Space Shuttle STS-1 through STS-39, and then witnessed twenty or so Space Shuttle launches after that. I have witnessed dozens of unmanned *Delta, Atlas, Titan* launches, including a dual *MX Missile* launch at Vandenberg Air Force Base in California. Seeing those launches was thrilling to my soul. The years from 1900 to 2001 were fascinating years saturated with discoveries, expeditions, and inventions. There was always something new and marvelous to look forward to enjoying in aviation space sciences and exploration. The great NASA astronomy missions of *Hubble Space Telescope (HST), Chandra X-Ray Telescope, Cosmic Background Explorer (COBE), Solar and Heliospheric Observatory (SOHO),* the *James Webb Space Telescope (JWST),* radio telescope missions, and others revealed to the people of my time that there is so much more order and infinite purpose to the Universe and for the existence of Mankind. Our perseverance in study, research, as well as social and religious debates, led us to develop our spacecraft and sensors to detect and record the evidence of how the Universe was designed. From that information, our minds have understood more of the meaning of life. We have a greater understanding of how expansive life must be and that the Universe does exist to provide an arena for life to perform the mysteries of experience.

I share my heart-felt compassion and love for the survivors of the *Challenger* 51-L Astronauts. Especially to the former Mrs. June Scobee, the widow of Commander Scobee. I know that she understands how delicate and precious human life is. I know that she realizes that life does go on after tragedies torment our emotions. Mrs. Scobee has lived through her tragedy and she is to be congratulated for achieving one of the most difficult parts of life—that of facing tragedy head-on in a personal and emotional way, and learning how to cope.

As a scientist, I believe we must stay focused on following the scientific method of exploring questions with observations, data gathering, testing, and formal proofs that utilize the tools and rules of the sciences. We must continue to propose ideas, contribute labor, and build machines and devices that enable humans to make observations, collect data, test and prove the answers to questions. This process is the method to discover the Laws of the Universe.

I respect the works and accomplishments of many explorers who preceded my life on Earth, such as: Galileo, Einstein, Orville and Wilbur Wright, Wernher von Braun, Robert Goddard, Euler, Bernoulli, Isaac Newton, Edwin Hubble, and Max Planc. Considering all aspects of life and the probability that death could be realized before the completion of a geographical exploration effort, I respect the accomplishments of the American explorers: Captain Meriwether Lewis, Lieutennant William Clark, and the Shoshoni Indian woman, Sacagawea. Those explorers and their team, *The Corp of Discovery* team, as they were officially called, conducted a phenomenal and historic expedition to discover a water passage from the Mid-Western United States to the North Western United States. Their commitment, bravery, application of human skills and practical senses, and successes in interfacing with human beings from unfamiliar cultures are exemplary of how the ultimate human is revealed when exercised by the joys and burdens of extreme exploration expeditions.

Lewis and Clark never discovered a water passage that led all the way to the Pacific from

Missouri, but their experiences and understandings of life were of limitless and extraordinary value and worth. Exploration is an investment, not a gamble. It is an investment of money, time, and efforts spent to examine the realities of what exists in the wilderness. Our fantasies of what could be out there in the unexplored parts of the Universe make the journey of discovery exciting and satisfying. It is the journey that is so exciting. Discoveries that we uncover satisfy our curiosities and give each of us fulfillment about our lives. Lewis and Clark would have known inherently from their exploration methods and experiences what 'The Truth About *Challenger*' means.

They knew the "Truth" because they were made from the same character traits from which all great people are made–fibers of hard work, following orders that are based upon what is right, and following basic rules of survival for safety and security of all living creatures. Great people exhibit curiosity, creative ingenuity, sacrificial traits that take risks for the good of all, sharing of one's life to enrich other lives, and the willingness to understand that the voyage is beyond all accountant estimates of value and worth. *The Corp of Discovery* was very diverse and was comprised of all those characteristics.

As explorers, we must apply what I call *practical sense*, not common sense. Many times common sense is merely what is commonly known amongst the population. Explorers, research scientists, and engineers fly ahead of the common knowledge and experience. Common sense invites the past to become the present. *Practical sense* invites and tempts the future to reveal itself.

I encourage explorers of the future to be *an explorer who is one-third engineer, one-third scientist, and one-third practical sense practitioner.* Explorers who will be like this will find the really marvelous discoveries, make useful sense of them, and build useful product from the discovery.   Space exploration activities are sophisti-cated indicators of how well humans understand the sciences.   Our lifestyles and our physical health are living proof of how practical we have become in applying what we have learned about science and our participation in the Universe.

The people of America may throw away one of the greatest treasures from the 20th Century, the NASA Space Programs.   The voyage into the expanses and stunning beauty of space for curiosity and pure exploration may have become only the past events of the history of America. I feel that The Journey has only begun.

The *Challenger* 51-L experiences provoked intense emotions and feelings of sadness, fear, lost dreams, and the needs for friendship and acceptance. From the conception of the Space Shuttle, through the design, assembly and test phases, repeated space flights, and the STS-25 (or 51-L mission), *Challenger* inspired my generation during an age of discovery.

CHAPTER 21

THE TRUTH
ABOUT *Challenger*

TRUTH - *A particular belief or teaching regarded by the speaker as the true one. The quality of being in accordance with experience, facts, or reality.   Conformity with fact.   Reality; actual existence. Agreement with a standard, rule, etc. (Webster's Dictionary)*

As I write these words for this chapter, I am forty-two years of age. I have invested thirty-seven of those years pursuing the intellectual and laborious process of mastering human flight for exploration and discovery.   The past twenty years I have worked professionally in aerospace and aviation, and I have been fortunate to witness so many historical developments of aviation and space flight. I have learned the answer to the question, "Why does Mankind have the relentless curiosity and the desire to pursue sustained flight and to explore?" The answers to this question are also pertinent to the question, "What is The Truth About *Challenger*?" Is there just one thing, or are there many truths that characterize the events and the lessons to be remembered about the last flight and mission of that great flying machine?

'The Truth About *Challenger*' is that the Universe is an awesome expanse of creation that we are only beginning to understand and experience. The Truth About *Challenger* is that NASA is your agency, regardless which nation you consider home and citizenship. NASA shares with the entire world what the space program workers of all job types have learned. NASA is an agency of typical people and gifted people who go about the laborious tasks of accomplishing the missions that have been determined to be the priorities of the technical and curious notions of Mankind. Perhaps no other working team has accomplished so much with the small percentage of wealth and political limitations that have been placed upon the NASA agency throughout its history.

'The Truth About *Challenger*' was contained and expressed in the eyes and smiles of the 51-L crew as they felt the power and authority of the *Challenger* as her rocket motors thundered and she ascended one last time from Pad B on that fateful day of January 28, 1986. For those brief moments of 73 seconds before total destruction, the 51-L Crew felt the full dose of the meaning of the Truth About *Challenger*. The Astronauts did not die in vain.

'The Truth About *Challenger*' is that we should never give up or cave-in on ideas and efforts that unselfishly strive to assist and make peace for people. 'The Truth About *Challenger*' is that many things in life are very difficult to accomplish. Those difficult things are not accomplished without a risk or focused dedication. NASA is a leader in doing the difficult and seemingly impossible feats of research, exploration, and discovery. NASA employees generally have the attitude that whatever the mission is, they will become the workers who will make the dream a reality.

Attitude has very much to do with 'The Truth About *Challenger*.' A person's attitude about themselves, other people, and the world around them, governs reactions to such colossal events as the *Challenger* Tragedy. People who have an attitude of distrust of government react to the *Challenger* Tragedy in a manner that says, "The government screwed up again and why should we continue to fund their antics?" On the other hand, people who appreciate dangerous and spectacular accomplishments will understand that NASA has succeeded and shared in so many areas of exploration, technological developments, and education in a vast spectrum of the sciences. Anyone who totally condemns NASA and its history is either living in a level of ignorance, or has an attitude disorder. I believe that most reasonable people, who recognize the qualities of dedicated effort and devotion, can understand that NASA occupies the lead position in technological achievements of this planet and its people. That is The Truth About *Challenger*.

'The Truth About *Challenger*' is that the *Challenger* Tragedy will be remembered in the future more frequently than, for example, the STS-2 Mission. STS-2 was the first time in the history of the world that a reusable spaceship, *Columbia,* was used the second time, *Columbia* having flown successfully on STS-1. In the future, people will be more captivated by the *Challenger* 51-L Mission Tragedy than the STS-2 Mission. For the record and in a technical sense, STS-2 was by far more important and rewarding to the NASA space flight team of engineers and Astronauts than was the *Challenger* Tragedy. The new Space Shuttle vehicle technical difficulties, the all-new designs and components, the high level of risks, the unknowns, and the precious cargo of people, made STS-2's successful flight much more exciting. Always remember, NASA was, and hopefully will always be, an agency devoted to goals, excitement, hard work, persistence, and success—not an agency of complainers and crybabies. Historically NASA has been an agency of reliable people who continually commit to doing their best work with all resources available, and to invent resources not yet developed.

In a team effort, NASA workers instinctively chart their own course and speed to success. The course is usually throttled back by Congress due to politics, funding limitations, or lack of understanding by the powerful politicians.

It is all too easy to sit in one's comfortable living room and criticize NASA for the unfortunate happenings that are events governed by probability. There is always a chance that something may go wrong with anything. The human element always increases the likelihood that something could go wrong.

Why even have a government or industry? What is it all for? All of us could argue for more or less government, more or less industry, to stay in our cradles as overgrown babies. However, wasn't it ourselves who cried and begged for our parents to free us from the confines of our own cribs in order to explore the world that our human senses detected? Can you recall how we also wanted to explore the unknown world just beyond the nursery door, just in the yard, or just across the street? That natural, inbred characteristic that drives us to realize new experiences is why *Challenger* was designed, built, and flown – for exploration.

What is the proper way to manage NASA in the future? Perhaps the best approach to the question is to just accept the proverbial risks of exploration and research, minimize risks where possible, implement the best ideas at the top of the priority list, and allow everyone to do their jobs with encouragement, training, recognition, and support. That is The Truth About *Challenger.*

What did you feel when you saw or heard about the crash of *Challenger*? Was the Tragedy made more tragic because of the horror and loss of human life?

Why do we feel so emotional about this kind of Tragedy? If we can feel so strongly when Tragedy takes the lives of people, why do we tend not to feel such strong emotions about our fellow men, women, and children of this Earth during normal times?

As I reflect back to the events of the *Challenger* 51-L Mission, the crew, the payload, the politics, the technology, and the crash, I know why Space Shuttle Commander Dick Scobee and his crew took the risks to fly into space. The risks were worth it to them because of the thrills associated with seeing the Universe from Earth orbit, and for the privilege to contribute to the many missions that must be accomplished to explore the Universe. The Truth About *Challenger* was as real as it gets to the *Challenger* Astronauts who paid the greatest sacrifice, *their lives.*

Another experience in my exploration work that has further taught me 'The Truth about *Challenger*' is the result of my time and efforts invested following up on the activities of Space Shuttle payload programs that I helped to process, launch, and recover during my time with NASA and the Space Shuttle Program. This work experience became my reality because I was seeking more from my space exploration career and because I made the decision and took the initiative in my life to spend my own money and my own time to learn and do, learn and do, learn and do.

In April 2000, I was invited to attend an astronomy symposium that was called, *"Ten Years of Hubble Telescope Science In Review."* The *Hubble Space Telescope* was launched into Earth orbit aboard Space Shuttle *Discovery* in 1989. The symposium was held at Johns Hopkins University in Baltimore, Maryland at the Space Telescope Science Institute (STSI). Having been a member of the *Hubble Space Telescope* processing and launch teams at KSC, I was fortunate to be allowed a seat to participate in this historic and educational review of advanced physics, astronomy, chemistry, and mathematics.

The lecturers and the audience were composed of engineers, scientists, astronomers, reporters, and Astronauts. The attendees were from Christian, Jewish, Hindu, Moslem, Atheist, and Humanism faiths and traveled from most countries of the world. The sciences are truly a common bond of people from all walks of life around the world. The new information that was presented at the symposium was absolutely awesome in its scope, revelation, and magnificence. The *Hubble Space Telescope (HST)* has given the Human Race a close look at the results of the *Big Bang* that preceded the expansion of the Universe. The *Hubble Space Telescope* has imaged objects that are at a great distance of a Red Shift of 14. This is a distance so vast that it is pointless to write it in scientific notation. Writing the number down will not make the objects any closer. The observed objects are spectacular systems such as black holes, novae, supernovae, nebulae, aurora, stars, and galaxies upon trillions of galaxies. There is no way to count all of those phenomenal systems because we cannot even see them all. Massive galaxies much larger than our own Milky Way Galaxy are infinitely plentiful and are moving away from the center of the Universe at speeds that approach the speed of light in a vacuum.

So much has been learned about astronomy and the Universe during the decade of the 1990s that many theories of classical astronomy from the 1900s have been proven to be inaccurate and have since been replaced. The new observations made by using the *HST, the Chandra X-Ray Telescope*, and powerful high-resolution radio telescopes around the world have challenged scientists to explain the phenomena that appear in the observations. Many of the challenging questions pose concerns as to whether what we see with a hi-tech telescope can be validated by the physics we know. Observations in our Universe that have been made by the *HST* may have discovered objects and systems that could be controlled by physics laws that perhaps we have not discovered.

That symposium is the most significant scientific event that I have ever attended. All of the humbling knowledge that was shared with the world was made possible by all of the efforts and sacrifices given by people from the past in research and development in the sciences that led to the amazing *Hubble Space Telescope*. The NASA team at KSC achieved the successful launch of the *HST* by following the *NASA Method*. This new era of efficient sharing of knowledge of the new findings of astrophysics and astronomy is also in part due to the successful launches of payloads aboard the Space Shuttle and various unmanned rockets. The great explorers who built and flew the Space Shuttle helped to make the annual astrophysics symposium at Johns Hopkins University possible. Without successful processing and launching of the telescope, the obser-vations made from the telescope would have never been realized. The Space Shuttle has launched the *HST* to Earth orbit and has serviced the telescope several times since then. The ability to change and improve the functional nature of the telescope has provided an observation flexibility that surpasses all telescopes that have ever been used by astronomers and astrophysi-cists.

NASA and the Astrophysics community of scien-tists are currently designing the *Next Generation Telescope (NGST)* now renamed the *James Webb Space Telescope*

(JWST). The *JWST* is affectionately called the *"Extra-Terrestrial Finder"* or *"ET-Finder"* because the telescope sensors will search for evidence and physical indication of planets the size of Jupiter and smaller Earth-like planets.

The *JWST* will certainly reveal thousands of planets within our Milky Way Galaxy and one can only imagine the celestial treasures to be revealed. As of 2002, we have only detected approximately 85 Jupiter-size or larger planets by detecting and measuring the Doppler Shift of the light emitted by the star. The amount of Doppler Shift or "wobble" is directly related to the mass of the planets tugging and pulling on the star as the planets orbit. Best estimates are that five percent of stars have planetary systems, so it is under-standable that *JWST* will make the search for planets efficient and more reliable.

We know that the location of a planet greatly determines the survival of organic life such as plants, animals, insects, microorganisms, and of course, humans. Realtors have been right for years by saying, "Location is everything." If Earth were to move just a few million miles (or about 5-10%) closer to our Sun, Earth would become like Venus—an oven of 920°F. due to the "Greenhouse Effect." If Earth were to move 5-10% away from the Sun toward Mars, Earth would become a frigidly cold planet like Mars. The tempera-tures on Mars rarely rise above zero degrees Fahrenheit. Conditions that support organic life forms such as humans are unique in the wide-open ranges of space. Those conditions are characterized and are detectable by looking for the balance of astrophysics (biology, chemistry, and astronomical makeup) of the stars, planets, and moons. By understanding the history and functions of our solar system, we can compare every other solar system that we observe and measure to our own familiar baseline solar system.

Understanding the conditions of how our own lives continue to survive and reproduce is being revealed like never before because humans have had the spirit to conceive, design, and fly sophisticated vehicles and instruments like *Apollo, Space Shuttle, Chandra X-Ray Telescope, Cosmic Background Explorer (COBE)*, and other space and Earth-based instruments.

Another Truth About *Challenger* has manifested itself in the area of teamwork amongst scientists and engineers. Something wonderful began to happen during the 1990s to accelerate exploration of the Universe. The sciences of astronomy and biology have now combined and a new science field is called *Astrobiology*. Astrobiology incorporates and integrates astronomy, chemistry, paleontology, geology, biology, mathematics, physics, astrophysics, and computer science to support exploration. The communications between scientists, engineers, technicians and financial supporters has eliminated traditional barriers and partitions of the working world that have kept scientists in separate labs and at a half-throttle efficiency. Working together to understand the Universe is what science is all about.

What is The Truth About *Challenger*? That Truth has everything to do with exploration, curiosity of the Human Race, and the search for answers to our ignorance that yields yet infinitely more questions about our lives, our Universe, and our creation. Why do people risk their lives to explore? Why have a Universe if we have no desire to discover and experience its grandeur?

Exploration of the Universe and the sciences has brought the world closer together in the partnerships that have formed to support the financing and participation of exploration. The enemies of the past do not seem like an enemy when we work together in space. There is room for us all "on the good Earth," as the *Apollo* 8 Astronauts stated from orbit around the Moon in December 1968.

The Truth About *Challenger* has to do with sharing the joy and excitement of research and development of the machines and tools that we need to explore the Universe. The financial and technical sharing is inevitable and it is justified. What inspires or benefits any man to rise up in unjustifiable anger against another man? There are no benefits in that angry or vicious kind of behavior toward each other. Exploration of space is the totally humbling quest that could finally challenge all of Mankind to determine if peaceful cooperation is possible.

My favorite elected leader of Federal government of the United States is President James Madison because of his practical sense, his loyalty to the establishment of America's self-governing form of government, and the passionate wisdom he had. At 75 years of age, Madison stated:

> *"The finiteness of the human understanding betrays itself on all subjects, but more especially when it contemplates such as involve infinity. What may safely be said seems to be, that the infinity and time of space forces itself on our conception, a limitation of either being inconceivable; that the mind prefers at once the idea of self-existence of an invisible cause possessing infinite power, wisdom and goodness, than to the self-existence of the Universe, visibly destitute of these attributes, and which may be the effect of them. In this comparative facility of conception and belief, all philosophical reasoning on the subject must perhaps terminate."*

In my experiences working with rocket

engineers, Astronauts, and leaders of exploration, I recognize that Madison understood the essence of The Truth About *Challenger*. This proves once again that Dr. Albert Einstein was correct in stating, "The only difference between the past, the present, and the future is an illusion." Madison lived and died decades before the *Challenger* 51-L Mission was launched, but he understood the Truth without the Space Shuttle *Challenger* being present. Our expensive toys of technology just help us to re-measure what has already been cut.

The *Challenger* Tragedy was merely a "stumping of the toe of civilization in the dark." That Tragedy will pass, but not be forgotten. The *Challenger* 51-L Astronauts are in our hearts forever. Their mission, 51-L, will be on some of our minds forever. We explorers of the 20th Century have provided the simple example to all people of the future that science, engineering, and exploration are realities that are built upon contributions of successes and failures from previous generations. Those dedicated contributions are the roadways for the curiosities of the next generations.

Without understandable evidence of how life began, humans develop theories of life's origin as they continue the scientific search for the apparent missing evidence, or humans trust by faith that life was created at some point. Leading astronomers, astrophysicists, biologists, and engineers I know and currently work with generally believe that the energy, space, gases, dust, rock, planets, and stars developed first and life became detectable later. However, this is merely a logical belief. Astrophysical and astrobiological exploration of the Universe will ultimately discover what the Truth of our history is.

As of the end of the 20th Century, humans have merely sampled the Universe with spacecraft and tools that will be considered primitive by explorers of the future. The belief that life developed last seems credible in that life, as humans typically think of life, is vulnerable to the powerful macro-forces of the constantly changing Universe. Life is delicate. Life is vulnerable.

Curiosity, imagination, and the thrills of exploring were the relentless forces that lured the *Challenger* 51-L crew to be in those ill-fated seats on January 28, 1986. As people around the world watched the *Challenger* 51-L Mission launch from the Earth, many of us were symbolically in those seats as our own spirits and fantasies of exploration thundered off the launch Pad with the *Challenger* Astronauts. If life exists to explore, discover, and enjoy the products of creation and science, as I have faith in God that it does, then we must continue to embrace and protect this human legacy of exploration that ignites our spirits, nourishes our souls, and humbles our minds. That *is The Truth About Challenger*.

<u>All That Is Around Us</u>

So, you say you want to fly?
You say you want to explore?
I know of places that have more, and more.

Those places are all around you.
They wait for you to wonder.
The secrets of creation are just beyond your senses.
Travel there and visit, new friends they will become.

Creation was made for you — to discover.
Like laughing children, we sing our songs of life.
Overcoming our limitations,
We use our instruments and craft to explore.
Let's launch now, so that we can enjoy.

Time seems to be a curse, the limitations of our desires.
But with our dreams and imaginations, we are always there.

All that is around us.
Just waiting for us to appear.

Randy Avera
1999

Future Exploration of the Universe
(Author's Recommendations)

Submitted January 28, 2003 to:
The United States Congress
The President of the United States

(The Centennial Year of First Flight)

1. Remove the NASA charter from *Title 42 of the Public Health and Welfare Codes* and create a new code for a revised NASA charter. The revised NASA charter must have a requirement that the U.S. Congress and the Office of the President adequately fund NASA so that the agency can be successful in achieving the programs without having to cope with understaffing of a skilled workforce and lack of equipment.
2. Replace aging electrical wiring in *Columbia*, *Discovery*, *Atlantis*, and *Endeavour* Orbiters.
3. Construct four new Shuttle Orbiters to support the current NASA business plan.
4. Construct a third launch Pad, Pad 39C, north of Pad 39B at Kennedy Space Center.
5. Authorize and allocate new funding to record and preserve the knowledge of aerospace workers who leave or retire from NASA and contractors. Recruit more of the most skilled archivists and historians in the world to lead us in documenting meaningful history.
6. Establish new challenging unmanned missions to Mercury, Venus, Earth, Mars, Jupiter, Saturn, Uranus, Neptune, and Pluto to focus upon astrobiology, geology, and energy.
7. Establish an International Base to house 50 humans on the dark and the illuminated sides of the Earth's

Moon to conduct astronomy, astrobiology, physics, geology, and low-gravity science and medicine.

8. Provide an Earth-Moon shuttle for people and cargo. This shuttle will be the first "space camp" training program to actually be in space. In addition to a cargo and people mover vehicle, this shuttle will take students into space for a field trip of a lifetime. Teach students in space. Allow states and private sector to help finance the program. Let the students work as understudy cooperative students to build, launch, and fly mission shuttles. Those students will be ready to discover the expanses of the Universe when they graduate from such programs.

9. Establish a national effort similar to the *Apollo* program to develop new engine, instrumentation, and flight guidance systems for rockets and spacecraft. New discoveries will reduce the cost of space launches, and hundreds of thousands of people will have meaningful jobs.

10. Establish a NASA/Center for Disease Control program for *Excellence In Space Medicine Research* that will encourage, guide, and mentor medical students, professors, college administrators, and practicing doctors to develop experiments and products for research in space.

11. Develop Virtual-Presence Robots to service the *James Web Space Telescope* that will be located in L-1 orbit far from Earth. No space telescope is perfect and maintenance is required for any sophisticated machine. The *JWST* is no exception. The alternative to robot mechanics is a Space Shuttle mission to L-1 orbit to service the *JWST*.

12. Provide a Super Telescope Base on the dark side of the Earth's Moon. This telescope base will exceed the technologies of *Hubble Space Telescope* and be even more flexible and convertible for varied observations and applications. The motto for the Super Telescope Base could be *"There is always something to see in the dark."*

13. Provide programs to rapidly increase space-based serviceable observatories in the X-Ray, Infrared, Ultraviolet, and Visible light spectra. The design and operational specifications for these observatories should require many orders of magnitude greater optical sensitivity and resolution than present day observatories.

14. Provide funding for the study of aurora atmospheric physics that occur on planets in our solar system, particularly Jupiter and its moon, Io. Answers to our energy problems are to be discovered by learning how aurora function.

15. Provide for a new, unmanned, Heavy Lift Vehicle (HLV) similar to the 1989 proposal for *Shuttle C* in 1989. A very practical payload weight-to-orbit design specification is 210,000 pounds cargo load. The rocket's payload compartment design diameter should be approximately 33 feet. The *Shuttle C* will provide lower cost heavy lift of cargo to Low Earth Orbit and save Space Shuttle flights for important human-presence missions.

16. Reactivate many of the U.S. National Testing Laboratories that have been closed during the 1990s. The loss of these laboratories has crippled the U.S. capability to develop reliable and safe space vehicles and commercial aviation safety enhancements.

17. Restore the NASA Quality Control system that existed during the *Apollo* program and implement that program into all NASA programs. Streamline the ways of old with validated better ideas and equipment for quality control work. Make NASA the world leader again in quality control.

Challenger Mission 51-L Astronaut Pilots and Mission Specialists on Flight Deck of Orbiter Simulator at Johnson Space Center. Seated L-R: Pilot Mike Smith, Mission Specialists El Onizuka and Judy Resnik, Commander Dick Scobee.
(NASA JSC photo December, 1985).

Challenger Mission 51-L Astronaut Mission Specialists and Payload Specialist in the Mid Deck of the Orbiter Simulator at Johnson Space Center. L-R: Backup Payload Specialist Barbara Morgan, *Teacher-In-Space* Christa McAuliffe, Hughes Payload Specialist Gregory Jarvis, and Mission Specialist Ron McNair.
(NASA JSC photo December, 1985).

Challenger being lowered into High Bay 3 of the Vehicle Assembly Building (VAB) at KSC for attachment to the External Fuel Tank (ET) for the first flight of *Challenger*, STS-6. Orbiter *Challenger* finally became a Space Shuttle just hours after this photo when the NASA/contractor team successfully mated the Orbiter to the ET. Randy Avera was the NASA Orbiter structures engineer working this operation.
(NASA KSC photo November, 1982).

Pad arrival photo of Space Shuttle *Challenger* sitting atop the Mobile Launch
Platform at Launch Pad 39B. This view clearly shows the large steel attach linkage
spanning the space between the defective Right Hand Solid Rocket Booster (SRB)
and the lower section of the External Fuel Tank (ET) where the liquid hydrogen fuel
is stored. This is the attach linkage that was melted and severed due to the deadly
escaping flame from the SRB Field Joint just above the linkage.
(NASA KSC photo).

Icicles hanging from the lower sides of the steel grating platforms of Pad 39B's Fixed Service Structure (FSS). Photo taken during inspection of the Pad/MLP/Shuttle by The Ice Team led by Mr. Greg Katnick and Mr. Charlie Stevenson of NASA KSC. NASA engineering representatives from Marshall Space Flight Center were also part of the Ice Team. Note the red fire extinguisher water pipes that were the source of water that formed these icicles. The icicles were located about 50 feet from the Space Shuttle *Challenger.* Ice could damage the Shuttle's thermal insulation materials during ignition and liftoff and threaten the safety of flight for the vehicle, payload, and Astronauts. (NASA KSC photo January 28, 1986).

The Operations Intercom System (OIS) Station 7-11 encapsulated with ice. The NASA Ice Team procedure called for this OIS box to be used to communicate the Pad icing situation and status to the Launch Director and Mission Management Team in the Launch Control Complex at KSC and in Mission Control at JSC. The Ice Team resorted to using hand-held radios for that communication. (NASA KSC photo January 28, 1986).

The *Challenger* 51-L Astronauts in the Astro-van, with KSC Patrol escort, depart the Crew Quarters at the Operations & Checkout building for the last time. Note the sheet of ice on the asphalt roadway that was formed by water spray from a cooling tower and below freezing temperatures during the night of January 27, 1986. The building is where *Apollo* spacecraft were checked out, *Spacelab* was processed, Shuttle horizontal payloads were processed, and where "Scobes" and I spoke to those high school students in 1979. My first NASA office was on the second floor to the left. (Photo by Randy Avera).

Ice that had just been crushed by the Astro-van as the *Challenger* Astronauts continued the historic drive to Launch Pad 39B. I will never forget the sound of the ice being crushed by the Astro-van. (Photo by Randy Avera).

The NASA Astro-van passed right in front of me as I got my last actual view of the Astronauts. Scobee was waving to us spectators from the large windows as the Astro-van rolled on into space exploration history. The NASA KSC Headquarters building is in the distance. (Photo by Randy Avera).

PHOTO ON RIGHT

This is a very historical and revealing photo of Space Shuttle *Challenger's* liftoff from Pad 39B on January 28, 1986 at 11:38 A.M. Eastern Standard Time. The camera was located on the ocean-side of the launch Pad. Notice the golden glow of the SRB flame radiating the bottom of the ET and the black base of the Orbiter. Most importantly, notice the charcoal black soot and smoke to the right edge of the SRB at the base of the ET just above the ET lower dome section. That smoke is not supposed to appear. That smoke is the proof and remains of the synthetic rubber O-rings that were eroded and melted by the 6,000°F SRB flame that leaked under pressure from the SRB field joint due to structural rotation of the joint. (NASA KSC photo).

Liftoff of Space Shuttle *Challenger* from Launch Pad 39B. I was located between the Launch Control Complex (LCC) at the Press Site when I photographed this scene. The family and invited guests of Christa McAuliffe are seen standing on the bench seats located just beyond the bus. This view of a Shuttle launch from Pad B had never been seen before and was the reason that I brought my camera to work. This is an excellent view of *Challenger* executing the traditional "Roll Program" that orients the vehicle and navigation program for boost to orbit and orbit insertion. *Challenger* has climbed about 1000 feet at this point in Mission Elapsed Time.
(Photo by Randy Avera).

Challenger continues to climb toward space. It was at this point that I feel the Astronauts were enjoying the ride with smiles from ear-to-ear, and their inquisitive human eyes wide open recording every detail of their epic experience. The sky was cold and clear. Close inspection of the SRB flames reveals a flow disturbance on the left side of the flame as you view this photo. Recall that the Orbiter is on the opposite side of the flame in what is called the "Heads-Down Attitude" and the defective SRB is to the left as you look at this photo. (Photo by Randy Avera).

The cryogenic cloud of hydrogen and oxygen rapidly expand as the liquid propellants expand from a super-cooled liquid to a gas. This expanding gas cloud was at about 43,500 feet above the Earth. The SRBs crossed paths as they flew out of control in the sky over KSC and the Atlantic Ocean. Notice large pieces of the Space Shuttle emerging from the gas cloud on ballistic trajectories toward the Atlantic Ocean. The wind shears are indicated by the deviations in the white smoke trail of the SRBs.
(Photo by Randy Avera).

The gas cloud convolutes and expands. Localized conflagrations of explosives were active within the gas cloud, but there was no impulsive, Earth-shaking explosion. The total potential energy of the propellants was not released in a second, but rather over approximately 90 seconds from ignition of the Orbiter main engines on the launch Pad. The Orbiter *Challenger* was aerodynamically shredded, not exploded.
(Photo by Randy Avera).

The cryogenic gas cloud rapidly expands even larger as the wild SRBs begin to cross flight paths and form what was called "The Crab Claws Design" in the sky.
(Photo by Randy Avera).

The debris field had become very chaotic as the *Challenger* Crew Module and Astronauts arched over the top of the ballistic path and began freefall toward the Atlantic Ocean. The estimates are that the Crew Module attained a maximum altitude of 62,300 feet. The time from vehicle breakup to water impact was approximately 2 minutes and 26 seconds.
(Photo by Randy Avera).

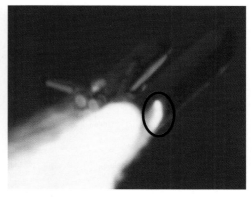

The SRBs were destroyed by this time. The expanding gas cloud is seeking thermal equilibrium. White vapor trails trace the paths of components of the Shuttle that contained gases such as liquid oxygen. I believe that all high performance manned rockets should have Escape Systems. Even if they had parachutes, the 51-L Astronauts could have bailed out at this point but at great risk of being struck by falling wreckage. A rocket-powered Escape System for the entire Crew Module is the solution. I would take an Escape System rocket ride from this chaotic mess in the sky any day. (Photo by Randy Avera).

A high altitude camera view that shows the right SRB with a flame 40 feet in length escaping from the defective field joint. This flame was melting and weakening the steel structural linkage that help secure and stablize the right SRB to the ET. The vertical tail and rudder of *Challenger* is visible to the lower left of the vehicle. The gorgeous morning sunlight is reflecting off the belly of *Challenger* just above the deadly SRB combustion leak. (NASA KSC photo).

This high altitude 70mm camera view shows the left SRB flying free.
(NASA KSC Photo).

The 70mm tracking camera located south of Pad 39B views the Crew Module stabilized aerodynamically and exerting no excessive forces on the Astronauts inside. The Crew Module forward windows are visible with the black thermal tiles around the windows. I say again, an Escape Rocket System like the design used for the *Apollo* spacecraft would have made the difference for the safety of the Astronauts. The Astronauts were most likely activating the Personal Egress Air Packs (PEAPs) at about this moment. (NASA KSC photo).

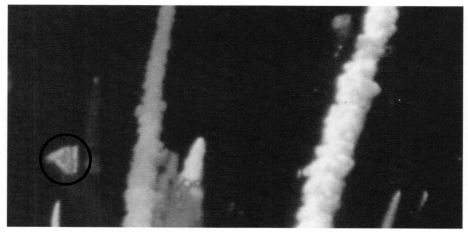

This view at 78.531 seconds Mission Elapsed Time reveals the triangular shaped left wing of the *Challenger*. (NASA KSC photo).

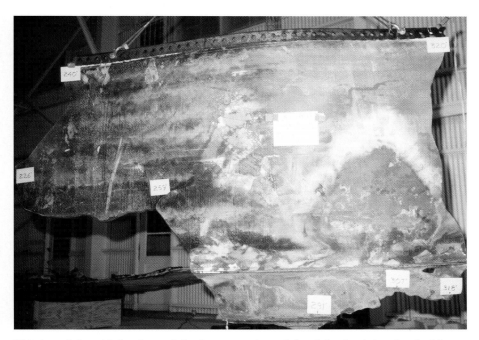

This is a 6 ft. x 10 ft. piece of the lower section of the defective joint that had been melted by the 6000°F flame that breeched the field joint of the SRB. The numbers indicate the degree positions that the flame melted. (NASA KSC photo).

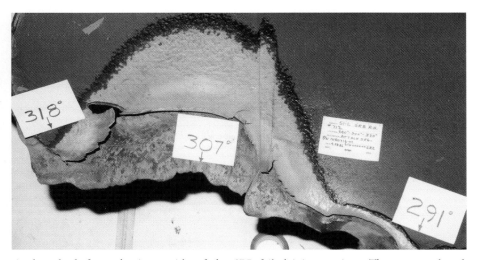

A close look from the inner side of the SRB failed joint section. The taupe-colored material is the thermal insulator that separates the SRB steel casing from the propellant. Typical failures of solid rocket motors are due to delaminations or separations of the insulator from the steel casing. That common failure mode was NOT the case for the Shuttle SRBs. (NASA KSC photo).

Seven black funeral hearses and one security car in procession carry the remains of The Seven *Challenger* Astronauts from Hangar L on the Cape Canaveral Air Force Station to the Shuttle Landing Facility (SLF) at Kennedy Space Center. The procession is shown headed north on State Road 3 just south of the Vehicle Assembly Building (VAB). It was peaceful and lonely that day as the Astronauts passed by me one last time, again in motor vehicles, and again with large windows like the Astro-van. This time, no one waved. Management leadership is critical to success of a program and to safe flight.
(Photo by Randy Avera, 1986).

The grave of *Challenger* Mission 51-L Commander Dick Scobee at Arlington National Cemetery with the Sun's rays symbolizing hope and life for those who have passed on from this life, and for those of us who remain in this life. Our character and respect for life is measured by how we treat each other. (Photo by Randy Avera).

The grave of *Challenger* Mission 51-L Pilot Mike Smith at Arlington National Cemetery. Mike was fortunate to have been the Pilot for Commander Scobee, a position that I would have been honored to serve. This rookie Astronaut learned The Truth About *Challenger* from the greatest people and from his own efforts. Mike was a loyal Astronaut who was living his dreams and ambitions to fly and explore. Mike's famous words "Uh-Oh!" indicated that he checked his instruments to the end. The character of loyalty to his work without fanfare was the Mike Smith we rocket engineers knew. (Photo by Randy Avera).

This test firing of the third redesigned SRB (or Solid Rocket Motor, SRM, as it is called during testing by Morton Thiokol) Qualification Motor, QM-6 occurred on April 20, 1988 at the Morton Thiokol's Wasatch Facility near Brigham City, Utah. This flame and smoke is from only one SRM. Rocket engineers always are in search of wide-open spaces such as deserts with mountains as flame deflectors. Although Morton Thiokol was caught in a web of design deception, there were many competent and dedicated workers who did their best efforts to design and build reliable and safe boosters. Private industry should never allow government Civil Service workers to sucker them into ethics of work problems that violate the public trust. (NASA photo).

Space Shuttle *Discovery*, STS-26, The Return To Flight Mission, takes the first steps toward PadB. *Discovery* and the Mobile Launch Platform were transported by the Crawler Transporter vehicle from the Vehicle Assembly Building at KSC. The view was thrilling because it expressed the look of space and was a space center healing in action. The July 4, 1988 U.S. Independence Day celebration was commencing just beyond the VAB door as *Discovery* rolled out. (NASA KSC photo).

Randy Avera (plaid western shirt, 23 years of age, 1½ years at NASA) works with his team of mechanics to develop the procedure that would install and remove the 6,000 pound Orbital Maneuvering System engine pods of the Orbiters. This hazardous operation transpires in the Orbiter Processing Facility at KSC and is vital to Orbiter maintenance between flights. This is evidence that engineers and mechanics make great teams if the environment promotes the relationship. Not shown were John Fraley (NASA), Lou Mavros (McDonnell Douglas St. Louis, Missouri), and John Tribe (Rockwell International) – my lead engineers and mentors for this important job.

The *Magellan* spacecraft that radar mapped Venus is shown installed into the Shuttle *Atlantis* at Pad 39B. We were preparing to close the Orbiter Payload Bay Doors for flight. The white cylinder with "USA" is the Interim Upper Stage (IUS) solid rocket booster for the *Magellan*.   The *Magellan* spacecraft is the portion located above the "USA" and supported by the white struts. *Magellan* utilized exotic manipulation of sensors and data processing to obtain the quantity and resolution quality of the Venetian images. Processing and launching *Magellan* was great fun and the mission revealed much new information about planets that form and become planets within the orbits of the Gas Giant planets like Jupiter and Saturn. Venus is completely covered with clouds of toxic gases and vapors like sulfuric acid, but *Magellan's* radar mapped the surface of Venus to a resolution that resolved objects as small as 300 feet in length.

This November, 1980 photo of Orbiter *Columbia* was taken on the night when we
installed the first Space Shuttle Main Engines (SSMEs). This historic moment was rocket
engineering at its finest. The three SSMEs were installed into the three large holes of
Columbia's aft fuselage base heat shield. Note the two Orbital Maneuvering System
(OMS) pods already installed (plastic engine bell protective covers shown). I was inspecting the equipment and general area from the platform in the upper right corner of the
photo prior to beginning the SSME installation operation. I wouldn't have missed this
event for any reason.

A pre-launch "thank you" from the *Discovery* STS-26 "Return To Flight" Astronauts. (NASA JSC photo).

Randy Avera in the right ejection seat of Orbiter *Columbia* in the Orbiter Processing Facility Bay 1 in 1981 after the historic STS-1 Mission that lasted two days and 48 orbits. *Columbia* had two ejection seats for the first five Shuttle flights only. The feelings of satisfaction and achievement were thrilling when I sat in the seat of the world's first spaceship after it's first flight, knowing that you and your colleagues made space flight history and that the Astronauts were at home, safe with their families. The Orbiters were my office and it was great to be back in that saddle again.
(NASA KSC photo).

In January, 1981, STS-1 Commander John Young and I took a moment from Crew Emergency Egress Training at the 195-foot level of Pad A to discuss aerodynamic interference concerns about the SRB cable trays and the elevon control surfaces on the wings of *Columbia*. John was quick to ask direct questions about technical matters that he was evaluating for flight test decisions. Both John and I were educated Georgia Institute of Technology in Aerospace Engineering, graduating 25 years apart. Today, both John and I are getting gray hair – that distinguished space cowboy look. Everyone needs a hero and John has been mine for decades. (NASA KSC photo).

This October, 1985 view of Space Shuttle *Atlantis* Mission 51-J for the U.S. Department of Defense is about as beautiful as Shuttle launches ever look. It is so fulfilling and satisfying to see what we have built flying so well.

Orbiter *Atlantis* Mission STS-30 approaches the threshold of the runway at Edwards Air Force Base, California after successfully deploying the space probe, *Magellan,* that was boosted to the planet Venus to radar map 99% of the Venetian surface. Note the landing gear deploying and the slight separation of the panels in the rudder/speed brake just above the engines (SSMEs). This mission was highly successful and *Magellan* was designed with spare parts to save costs. The *Magellan* used very complex data processing and manipulation techniques to acquire maximum data from the cheap spacecraft as it scanned the surface of Venus. This mission led to the topographical scanning of Earth years later. It was my great honor to have worked on this Mission. (NASA photo)

A rare view of Orbiter *Discovery* Mission 51-C, January, 1985, on approach to the KSC Shuttle Landing Facility (SLF). We pilots love this photo with the runway just below, gear "down and dirty", attitude just right for a smooth landing at 212 miles per hour (183 knots). (NASA KSC photo).

This was a day that I will never forget when *Challenger* made its first landing on the dry lakebed soil of Edwards Air Force Base, California at the end of Mission STS-6. Notice the white air-stair on the port side of *Challenger* for the Astronauts to exit the Orbiter, the yellow tow-bar on the nose gear, the wheels impressed into the soil, and the small black Orbiter/ET umbilical door located just left of the main landing gear open to the purge position. We rocket engineers were so pleased with *Challenger's* flight performance that week and it would continue to compete with *Columbia* for best Orbiter in the world. (NASA photo).

A rare view of the Orbiter Side Hatch, or Crew Module access door, as seen from the Edwards Air Force Base lakebed. The day was so memorable with the deep blue California sky and low humidity which we Florida boys and girls enjoyed. The aluminum tool for handling the hatch is only used after landing to make opening and lowering the door easy in order to egress the Astronauts. Note the angle of the streaks on the black tiles. That angle is approximately 40 degrees from horizontal and correlates to the 40 degree nose-up attitude of the Orbiter for the hot reentry through the Earth's atmosphere. This view is just how *Challenger* looked as we worked the recovery operations. The name *Challenger*, the Commander's side and middle window, the payload bay door hinge, the "Rescue" arrow, and the Side Hatch window are very sexy to me. You have to be an aviator or an explorer to know what that means. Spaceships are very sexy, powerful, and majestic. (NASA photo).

Talk about powerful and majestic, lean and mean. *Challenger* was just plain sexy. I really love this view of the magnificent flying machine. Note the milky haze on the Commander's forward window pane that was causes by out-gassing of the tile system and from the separation rocket motors of the SRB that fire to control the motion of the SRB as they separate from the Shuttle at 2 minutes and 20 seconds into flight to orbit. (NASA photo).

This is a spectacular view of *Challenger* Mission 41-B (STS-11) after landing at KSC. This was the first Shuttle mission that was launched at KSC and landed at KSC. The recovery safety team is inspecting and sensing the Orbiter and local area for explosive or toxic gases and liquids prior to approving our team of mechanics, engineers, and operations people to recover and de-service the Orbiter. The white trucks are the Freon Cooling System for the avionics aboard the Orbiter (behind left main gear), and the Portable Purge Unit (behind the three safety inspectors). Note the white vapor jetting from the starboard side of the vertical tail. That is not good. The Amonia Spray Boiler System (that cools avionics below 100,000 feet) had a malfunction that was producing that hazardous condition. (NASA KSC photo).

Orbiter *Challenger* quakes the Earth below Pad A at KSC in April, 1985 as it clears the launch tower moments before executing the characteristic Roll Program ballet in the sky. The $5 billion *Spacelab* module for medical, and physics research is inside the cargo bay. (NASA KSC photo).

This is my favorite and most haunting photo of Orbiter *Challenger*. I was there when this photo was taken at Edwards Air Force Base, California in 1983, STS-6. There was no wind, no distracting sounds, and *Challenger* was in all its glory, humbly basking in the sunshine, having completed its first orbital flight and mission successfully. This was very historic in that the second Orbiter ever built demonstrated repeatability of safe flight for a different tail number, OV-099, the old Structural Test Article, STA-099. Note the black line in the soil that is motor oil to define the centerline of the very wide dirt runway. *Challenger* looks very coy and innocent in this view and causes me to recall the successful times that we experienced with *Challenger*. The sounds and moments easily come to mind about the many great times we engineers, technicians, and Astronauts had building and testing *Challenger*. The fate of *Challenger*, the Astronauts, and the reputation of NASA would be tested with this great spaceship only two years later. The SRB design and performance problems had already determined the Tragedy yet to come in January 28, 1986. (NASA photo).

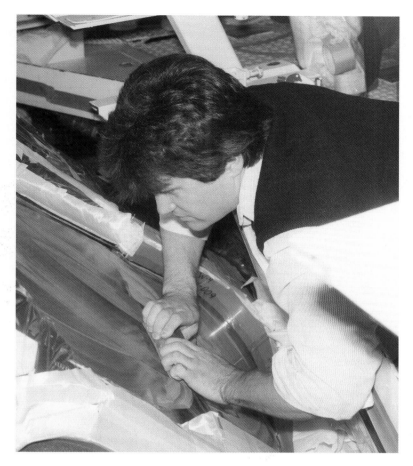

Rocket engineering is not always glamorous, but physics, chemistry, and materials sciences are fundamental to our work. Here I performed the first ever Orbiter window cleaning and polishing procedure for the forward fused silica glass windowpanes of Orbiter *Challenger* for the upcoming 41-C Mission. This procedure removed the milky haze that was deposited onto the pane from the exhaust of the SRB forward separation motors. This process, developed by NASA engineering (Chuck Wheelright JSC, and Randy Avera KSC), Gene Jensen (Lockheed Quality Engineering KSC), Col. Robert Mercer (SDIO Pentagon), and the loyal and dedicated Orbiter Forward Fuselage Technicians of KSC. The window requirements included pilot's visual, general photography visual, and window scratch limit specifications to prevent windowpane structural failure. Shuttle Orbiter windows were the largest in area ever flown and we wrote the book of physics, inspection, and maintenance for the complex system of Orbiter windows. I submitted Engineering Support Requests (ESRs) for window protective "Eyelids" to protect the panes during boost to orbit and on-orbit when not in use visually, but NASA decided not to upgrade the window design to solve those safety of flight issues.

Challenger 51-L flies free as the birds! The unusual number of seagull birds escort Space Shuttle *Challenger* and the Astronauts to their time and place in history just 67 seconds ahead. Human endeavors to explore our Universe require flight beyond the capabilities of Seagulls, and the risks and hazards of such flight are high. The best ways to avoid Tragedy and loss are to "Just <u>DO</u> your job," as Astronaut John Young says. "Just <u>DO</u> good work," as Astronaut Guss Grissom said. Randy Avera says, "Create meaningful rules and a system that applies the rules to accomplish the objectives, obey the rules, ensure accountability, and joyfully receive problems as the first step of creating new products and services unimagined."
(NASA KSC photo).

18. Establish a four-year accredited degree program with universities to educate and train Space Program Quality Engineers on a Co-Operative program. The same colleges can provide a two-year Associate degree in Quality Control Inspection. The degrees will state that the owner of the degree has achieved NASA's highest standards of excellence in Quality Control.

19. Provide a new *Office of Corporate Knowledge* that continually solicits ideas, recommendations, inventions, suggestions, and concepts and presents those resources to all NASA employees to foster a "build upon our ideas" lifestyle. The products from this Office will help NASA management to plan the programs of the future by truly playing the entire team in the effort.

20. Mandate an *Annual Management Review* of NASA management actions and problems to identify problems and solve them before they become tragedies. The Annual Management Review should be conducted in May of each year so that problems can be solved prior to going to the Taxpayers in October to ask for funding. NASA must be sure of its performance condition before asking for funding.

21. Develop new jobs and equipment that will assist cosmologists, astrophysicists, astronomers, and astrobiologists in the overwhelming task of analyzing the avalanche of technical data from space-based telescopes. Provide more funding and technology sharing with Radio Telescope Astronomy programs.

22. Provide new advanced training for spacecraft technician mechanics in avionics, electronics, basic chemistry, construction techniques, machining (manual and computer-based), and basic forensic inspection techniques and equipment for spacecraft.

23. NASA to provide leadership and funding for a new program to measure and study the chemistry, physics, and quantum mechanics of the Sun with special emphasis on how the Sun stores, converts, and transmits energy. The program would include space-based, Moon-based, and Earth-based observations of the Sun's Corona, the relative surface of the Sun, and the core of the Sun. The classical research applications of manipulations of light waves and light particles will continue to be used, but NASA will employ the newest of experimental and proven devices and methods of observing, measuring, and evaluating the light emitted from the Sun and the mass/gravity/energy relationships of the Sun. The data and knowledge gained from this program will be linked and compared to other solar and interstellar studies of stars other than the Sun.

24. NASA to provide leadership and funding for a program to extend our knowledge on *Anti-Matter, Dark Matter,* and *The Missing Baryons* (protons, neutrons, and electrons) to supplement what will be learned from the other NASA programs in the sciences of astronomy, energy, physics, biology, and chemistry. Overall, NASA will then be able to utilize supercomputers to define and model the development of the Universe regarding mass properties distribution, energy distribution, multi-degree of freedom dynamics, and what may actually be the fabrication of new volumes of space as the Universe continues to expand into the unknown.

25. NASA to provide leadership and funding for a research program to study the inter-relations of gravity, mass, and energy that will yield supplemental meanings and applications to work in physics, and for the General and Special Relativity cases that Dr. Albert Einstein discovered.

26. NASA to provide leadership and funding for research and development of Super-Conductors that will dramatically improve the efficiency and reliability of electrical and electronic circuits by reducing electron friction with the conductor and thereby reducing energy losses such as exothermic heat.

27.   NASA to provide leadership and funding to research and develop new machines for unmanned and manned exploration. The needs are for new inventions at the component and at the assembly levels to produce durable, multi-functional, and serviceable machines to retrieve geological and physical samples from planets, moons, and asteroids. The new machines will be designed for the proper amount of power, control, and dexterity to explore and excavate in hazardous liquids, solids, and gases.   Examples of extreme environmental conditions are those that exist on the outer planets and moons of our solar system. Liquid and solid oceans of methane do exist at very cold temperatures, high pressures, intense gravity fields, intense electromagnetic radiation, and volcanic and seismically dynamic conditions common to those solar system bodies.

28.   NASA to provide leadership and funding to transfer NASA's wealth of knowledge regarding human physiological and general medical science. One example of medical knowledge to share with the public is that involving the human inner ear/brain interactions that affect balance, equilibrium, and orientation.

29.   NASA to provide leadership and funding to develop programs, workshops, and certifications for advanced design, machining, manufacturing, and main- tenance of aircraft and spacecraft. This effort will teach technicians to become educated with the skills neces- sary to produce the great works required of Space Programs of the future.

30.   NASA to provide leadership and funding in the sciences of "micro-film" or "thin-film" technologies to boost the development of optical physics, electronics, manufacturing, and astronomy.

31.   NASA to develop/implement/operate regularly scheduled *Space Sciences Educational Workshops* at each NASA center to educate, motivate, and guide students toward efficient educational and career paths. The workshop credits would be transferable and provide quarter or semester hours for college credit. The workshops would be held at the many NASA facilities around the nation that are always available. The workshop could be three months in session and educate new high school and entry-level college students about NASA space programs and how to tailor their educational courses and summer break employment to a career in space exploration. The workshops should cover one month of space science history, one month of current technologies, and one month of what is needed to take the NASA programs to the next level of sophistication and productivity. The students will then be better prepared to select meaningful college courses, hobbies, and summer work experiences.

GLOSSARY

of

NASA ACRONYMS, SPACE PROGRAM TERMS, AND NASA "LINGO"

(*NOTE*: Some of these definitions are from Webster's New World Dictionary, Third Edition. Most of the definitions are original works by the author of this book.)

Apollo - The name of Greek Mythology's Sun god. This name was chosen by NASA and the United States Congress to be the official name for the Manned Program to the Moon.

Apollo Program - The Manned Space Program that sent Mankind to the Moon and return them safely to the Earth. The National Aeronautics and Space Administration developed and led the program during the 1960s and early 1970s. The *Apollo Program* included rocket and lunar transportation vehicle designs and development, facility construction, Astronaut training and launching of unmanned and manned missions to the Moon, and in specific mission cases, launches to Earth orbit. A total of six manned landings on the Moon were successful allowing twelve American Astronauts to walk upon the Moon's surface and to be returned safely to Earth. The program allowed Mankind to visit a celestial body other than Earth for the first time as recorded by the history of Earth. There is no conclusive evidence that any person has ever traveled to or visited another planet or star as of the date of this book copyright. Perhaps that will change in the near future.

Apollo Spacecraft - The section of the Moon rocket located at the top of the *Saturn V* rocket and was the cargo or payload for the *Saturn V* rocket to lift and propel to the Moon. The *Apollo Spacecraft* consisted of five major elements, the Command Module, the Service Module, the Lunar Module, the *Saturn* Lunar Module Adapter Shroud, and the small Launch Escape System (LES) rocket located at the very top of the *Apollo Spacecraft*.

Astronaut - An American term that identifies a person who has traveled to an altitude of at least 100,000 feet above the Earth's surface. The term means *Star Voyager*. In some cases, people who have been given the title of *Astronaut* after having been killed while in service with NASA. Mrs. Christa McAuliffe and Mr. Greg Jarvis were two of NASA's honorary Astronauts.

Astronomer - An expert in astronomy.

Astronaut Position Description - A job title or position at NASA held by people who have been selected by NASA to work those positions. The NASA Position Description, Astronaut, does not mean that the employee has yet flown above the 100,000 feet altitude definition of becoming an Astronaut.

Astronomy - The science of the Universe in which the stars, planets, etc. are studied including their origins, evolution, composition, motions, relative positions, sizes, etc.

APU - Auxiliary Power Unit, a subsystem of the Space Shuttle Orbiter that uses a fuel called hydrazine to run the APU that generates rotary motion to produce 3,000 pounds per square inch of pressure in the Orbiter hydraulic system. Each Orbiter has three APUs that independently provide pressure for the three independent Orbiter hydraulic systems.

Atlantis - The fourth *Orbiter* vehicle in a series of five Orbiters that have been built as of the end of the 1980s.

Aurora - Irregular, luminous phenomena, as streamers, visible at night in a zone surrounding the magnetic poles of a planet or moon that has an atmosphere. An Aurora is produced when atomic particles strike and excite atoms in the portion of the atmosphere called the Ionosphere.

Big Bang - The cosmic event that occurred in the smallest imaginable instant of time of the beginning of the Universe when there was an instantaneous creation or formation and release of energy and matter into three-dimensions. The quantities of energy and matter that were initially released by the Big Bang are equal, or constant, to the energy and mass that currently exist in the expanding Universe. Many astronomical and cosmological debates have been argued in search of the answers to whether space was already present for the energy and matter to expand into, or if the expansion of the energy and matter progressively created space in three dimensions. The Big Bang event produced the atomic elements called Baryons (protons, neutrons, and electrons, and the sub-atomic particles). As the expanding energy and matter cooled, the simplest atoms such as Hydrogen and Helium were formed. As the physics and chemistry of the cosmos developed further, larger atoms and molecules were formed that are the fundamental elements of chemistry as we understand that science today. It has been at least 14 billion years since the Big Bang occurred and the Human Race has only learned the elementary knowledge of chemistry of the Universe. Future generations will discover amazing laws and behaviors of the chemistry in the Universe.

Big Bang Theory - A former theory of how the Universe may have begun that was proven true in the 1980s and 1990s. The theory was proven to be true by the NASA space probe, Cosmic Background Explorer (COBE), that detected and measured the predicted value of the background radiation level that is the signature or "fingerprint" and evidence that the Big Bang did happen billions of years ago. The background radiation detected and measured by COBE has achieved a stable equilibrium of physics due to the billions of years of rapid expansion and cooling of the Universe after the Big Bang.

Biology – The science that deals with all living organisms such as plants, animals, insects, and fish. Biology deals fundamentally with life cycle processes and documents the variations of physical and chemical composition of the various forms of life on Earth.

Black Hole - A volume in galactic space in which massive quantities of matter including light are drawing inward, like a vortex, and exhibits extremely high magnitudes of gravity. That gravity force is so intense that light particles are restrained and cannot radiated outward from the Black Hole.

CAPCOM - An acronym for the "Capsule Communicator." The term originated in the early programs of the American Space Program. The CAPCOM is a person who is the single point of communication between the Astronauts in a rocket, as well as the launch and mission team. The CAPCOM minimizes confusion during the mission operations, and CAPCOM is usually another Astronaut who is familiar with the mission and procedures.

Challenger - The second Space Shuttle Orbiter vehicle in a series of five Orbiter vehicles that were built 75% complete in Palmdale, California by Rockwell International on Federal contract to NASA. NASA and its contractors (Rockwell International and Lockheed Space Operations Company) completed the remaining 25% of construction and preflight processing and checkout at the Kennedy Space Center in Florida.

Challenger Accident - A term commonly used by people who do not understand the history and events of the *Challenger's* structural breakup during the period of flight between 71 and 73 seconds into the 26th Space Shuttle launch at Kennedy Space Center, Florida. The *Challenger's* structural breakup occurred on January 28, 1986 and cost the lives of the seven Astronauts onboard. The word, accident, is not the correct application of the word for the *Challenger* Tragedy. The correct words are "crash" or "Tragedy" because the design flaws of the Solid Rocket Boosters (SRBs) were known well before the first Shuttle flight, but were allowed to fly.

Challenger Tragedy - The proper term used by people who do understand the history and events of the *Challenger* structural breakup during the 26th Space Shuttle launch. Tragedy is the proper term because the design flaws of the Solid Rocket Boosters (SRBs) were known prior to the first Shuttle flight, and the Shuttles were allowed to fly in that risky and hazardous configuration.

Chemistry – The science that deals with mass and energy by analyzing and measuring the interactions and laws of the elements, compounds, and solutions. Chemistry focuses upon the natural and man-made elements of the Periodic Table of the Elements and the equations and processes that control the combinations and breakdowns of those elements. Chemistry is fundamental in the process of living for organic organisms. Chemistry is fundamental in the non-organic elements of the Universe.

Close-out Crew - Contractor mechanics, technicians, and NASA Quality Control Inspectors who secure the Astronauts inside the Shuttle Orbiter Crew Module, and close the crew ingress/egress hatch for flight in accordance with the NASA countdown procedure

Columbia - The first Shuttle Orbiter vehicle in a series of five that have been built to date. On April 12, 1981, *Columbia* was the first Space Shuttle Orbiter of the fleet to fly. That historic flight began routine access to and from space for people and the cargo, or payload.

Complex 39 - A very large area of land and intercoastal water located at the north end of the John F. Kennedy Space Center, Florida. It spans from the Atlantic Ocean to the Indian River and includes the famous Mosquito Lagoon Wildlife Preserve, or protected area. Complex 39 includes two launch Pads (Pad A and Pad B) which

are the two active Space Shuttle launch Pads.   For
Shuttle service, those two launch Pads were converted
from the former *Apollo* Program Pads that launched all
of the *Saturn V* class boosters (or launch vehicles) that
propelled the *Apollo* spacecraft to the Moon for all of the
American lunar landing missions.   Complex 39 also
includes the voluminous Vehicle Assembly Building
(VAB) that was built for the *Apollo* Program to vertically
"stack" the *Saturn V* launch vehicle with the *Apollo* spacecraft atop the *Saturn V*.   The VAB was modified
internally to accommodate the Space Shuttle vertical
"stacking" operations and preflight vehicle integrated
testing.   Complex 39 also includes the Launch Control
Complex (LCC) that has control rooms called "firing
rooms."   The LCC supports preflight integrated tests
and checkout of the Shuttle and installed payloads, and
obviously, launch countdowns.   The Shuttle Landing
Facility (SLF) is located in Complex 39, just to the
northwest of the VAB.   This is a one of a kind 15,000
feet long runway for Shuttle landings and recovery
operations.   Complex 39 has other facilities for
engineering, maintenance, logistics, NASA railroad
service, and various technical support services, as well
as pyrotechnic storage bunkers.

Computer Science – The science dealing with computer
design, functions, technology developments for
computer speed, memory, human friendly interfaces,
networking of programs, and program development
technologies.

Contractor - A private company that is awarded
contract(s) to support government projects or
programs.

Crew Quarters - Facilities pro vided for Astronauts which house the administrative, living, and sleeping conveniences for Astronauts who are temporarily located at Kennedy Space Center in support of a Mission.

CSM - Command and Service Module. The section of the *Apollo* spacecraft that consisted of two major pieces of hardware: One piece was the Command Module that contained instruments, controls, food, and personal provisions for the Astronauts. The Command Module was the only portion of the *Apollo/Saturn* combination that was recovered after the module parachuted into an ocean on Earth. The other piece of the CSM was the Service Module that contained a single, highly reliable rocket engine that used hypergolic chemical propellants. The Service Module was cylinder-shaped and was attached to the rear of the cone-shaped Command Module. Additionally, there were other systems such as life support systems and a scientifically valuable payload instrument bay called the Scientific Instrumentation Module Bay (SIM Bay) where a high-resolution mapping camera was housed to map the Moon's surface as the CSM orbited the Moon.

Discovery – The Third Space Shuttle *Orbiter* vehicle in a series of five Orbiters that have been built during the 1970s and 1980s.

Endeavour – The Fifth Space Shuttle *Orbiter* vehicle in a series of five that were built. *Endeavour* was built to replace *Challenger* after the *Challenger Tragedy* of 1986. Most of the parts of *Endeavour* were spare parts that were required to exist by the original Space Shuttle Program contract with Rockwell International. The 5.5-billion dollars that were spent by NASA, as Executive Ordered by President Ronald Reagan, were to "spare the spare parts" that were consumed and to pay Rockwell International for constructing and testing the new *Endeavour.*

Enterprise – A Shuttle-like vehicle that looks similar to an *Orbiter* but cannot be boosted into Earth orbit due to design limitations. The *Enterprise* is not considered one of the five Orbiters that have been built in the 1970s and the 1980s. The *Enterprise* was built as a proto-type to the *Orbiter* fleet and was the Approach and Landing Test (ALT) drop test vehicle at Edwards Air Force Base in 1977. The ALT was a program that evaluated the subsonic flight characteristics of the *Enterprise* throughout the altitude range from 22,000 feet down to the final approach and landing. The Microwave Landing System (MLS), *Orbiter* computers, hydraulics, electronics, wheels and brakes, flight controls, mechanisms, and structures were systems that were evaluated by the ALT program. The *Enterprise* was used as a pathfinder at Kennedy Space Center to validate and verify the facilities that process the *Orbiters. Enterprise* was used at Marshall Space Flight Center (MSFC) in the Mated Vertical Ground Vibration Tests (MVGVT) to evaluate the dynamic responses of the entire Shuttle vehicle when stacked upon a launcher.

E T - External Tank, or External Fuel Tank. Also see *External Fuel Tank.*

Explore - To examine carefully, investigate, to travel in a region previously unknown or little known in order to learn about its natural features, inhabitants, etc.

Expanding Universe - The theory, notion, or fact of the matter within the Universe continues to expand three-dimensionally outward from its apparent origin from the *Big Bang*.

External Fuel Tank - The fuel tank that attaches to the belly of the Shuttle *Orbiter* and supplies liquid hydrogen and liquid oxygen propellants to the three Space Shuttle Main Engines (SSME) located in the rear of the *Orbiter*. The *External Fuel Tank* is the only part of the *Space Shuttle* that is not reusable. After nine and one-half minutes into flight, the *External Fuel Tank* is separated from the *Orbiter* and the tank burns up in a fiery reentry through the Earth's atmosphere over the Indian Ocean. Proposals have been made to boost the tank into a Low Earth Orbit to use the tanks for various purposes in the future. The *External Fuel Tank* is commonly referred to as the *ET*.

Facilities - Buildings and equipment.

Galaxy – A massive volume consisting of solar systems, individual stars, binary stars, comets, asteroids, interstellar gases (nebulae) dust particles, novae, super-novae, black holes, quasars, and pulsars. The Universe apparently contains uncountable numbers of galaxies that are constantly being born, maturing, dying, and recycling the matter and energy of the Universe.

GLS - Ground Launch Sequencer. A computer system located in the Launch Control Complex (LCC) and interfaces with the two Shuttle launch Pads. The Ground Launch Sequencer automatically controls and processes the final nine minutes of the countdown of a Shuttle launch. Thousands of computer commands and data are being processed for the launch as the GLS program runs.   The GLS allows the personnel in the LCC and at Mission Control in Houston, Texas to focus upon specific problems that might occur during the terminal count of the launch countdown.

Geology – The science that deals with the formation of the Earth by studying structural, chemical, and general physics of the Earth's crust, mantel, and lava flows.

HST - Hubble Space Telescope.

Hubble Space Telescope - A large, powerful, telescope that was launched into Earth orbit aboard a Space Shuttle *Discovery*, Mission STS-31, on April 24, 1990 to study many subjects of astronomy and astrophysics by making detailed high-resolution images of the objects viewed either in deep or near space. The design of the telescope is unique in that its electronic components can be removed and replaced to make the functions of the telescope varied. The *HST* is a telescope with many possible telescope configurations.

Integral – A mathematical term that sums and accounts for all of the area under the curve of a mathematical function.   This term also means the summation of efforts or actions.

Johnson Space Center (JSC) - The NASA Center in Houston, Texas that is responsible for the Space Shuttle design, Astronaut training, and controlling of the Shuttle Missions from after launch through *Orbiter* landing.

Kennedy Space Center (KSC) - The NASA Center at Kennedy Space Center, Florida that is responsible for processing, launching and landing recovery of *Space Shuttles* and their cargos known as payloads.

Landing recovery - The process of retrieving a Space Shuttle *Orbiter* from its landing on primary or on alternate runways that are located at many locations around the world. Landing recovery involves many hazardous operations with *Orbiter* and payload (cargo) systems. Landing recoveries that occur away from Kennedy Space Center involve mounting the *Orbiter* on the top of the NASA 747 aircraft called the Shuttle Carrier Aircraft (SCA) for transport to the Kennedy Space Center in Florida.

Launch - The action of initiating the powered flight of the Space Shuttle at Kennedy Space Center, Florida.

Launch window - The predetermined period of time during which a space vehicle can be launched to achieve proper trajectory or orbit, as determined by the Mission and payload requirements.

Launch turnaround - The amount of time and work required to recover from a scrubbed launch attempt that would result in full support activities for the next attempt of the same Mission.

LEM - Lunar Excursion Module. The LEM was a two-stage spacecraft designed to transport two *Apollo* Astronauts from orbit about the Moon to the surface of the Moon, and return to Lunar orbit. The first stage of the LEM was called the Descent Stage and had a very reliable rocket engine that was powered by hypergolic chemical rocket propellants. After the exploration of the Lunar surface was completed, the Astronauts were launched into Lunar orbit by the second stage of the LEM called the Ascent Stage. The Ascent Stage utilized the Decent Stage as a launching platform. A total of six

LEMs made soft landings on the surface of the Moon and safely returned twelve American Astronauts to Lunar orbit where the Command and Service Modules (Mother Ship) patiently waited in orbit.

LIOH Canisters - Lithium Hydroxide canisters provide a chemical process to remove, or scrub, carbon dioxide from the breathing air in the Crew Module of the Orbiter. The scrubbing of carbon dioxide from the air allows for the recycling of the breathing air which eliminates the need to carry large quantities of oxygen into space for the Astronauts to breathe.

Mankind - The Human Race: all women, men, and children of planet Earth.

Marshall Space Flight Center (MSFC) - The NASA space center located in Huntsville, Alabama that was responsible for the design and development of the Space Shuttle Solid Rocket Boosters (SRBs), the External Fuel Tank (ET), as well as the extensive history of rocket boosters, such as the *Apollo* Program's powerful *Saturn 1, Saturn 1-B, and Saturn V.*

MLG - Main landing gear located on the underside of the Space Shuttle Orbiter and provides structural support for the Orbiter during landing on a runway.

MLP - The Mobile Launch Platforms are massive steel structures that were designed for the *Apollo* Program to support the *Saturn V* rocket with the *Apollo* spacecraft during vertical "stacking" operations in the Vehicle Assembly Building (VAB), transport to the Complex 39 launch Pads, and vehicle processing and launch at the launch Pads. The MLP was converted from the *Apollo*

Program configuration to the current design configuration for Shuttle. The conversion of the MLP for Shuttle included substantial structural modifications to provide three flame holes and the provisions that secure the Shuttle to the MLP, and the various umbilical systems for cryogenics, electrical, and pneumatics. The MLP was also modified to include the Shuttle Sound Suppression water deluge system that protects the Shuttle and its onboard payload from the damaging forces generated by the acoustical energy at a noise level of 165 decibels from the Solid Rocket Boosters (SRBs). The MLP during the *Apollo* Program also supported the towering steel structure called the Launch Umbilical Tower (LUT) that provided access and umbilical support to the *Saturn V* and *Apollo* spacecraft. The Shuttle MLP design has the umbilical tower relocated off of the MLP and rigidly fixed to the concrete pad around the MLP. The Shuttle tower is called the Fixed Service Structure (FSS) and does not travel with the MLP between the pads and the VAB.

Mobile Launch Platform - See MLP.

Mission - The total objectives of a space flight. The Mission Objectives typically involve the launch, ascent to orbit, on-orbit, reentry, approach and landing phases of the space flight.

Moon - A celestial body that orbits a planet.

Moon, The - The proper noun that identifies the only Moon that orbits our planet Earth.

MSFC – Marshall Space Flight Center in Huntsville, Alabama

NASA - The National Aeronautics and Space Administration.

NASA Headquarters - The NASA organization in Washington, DC that is responsible for the *Space Shuttle Program* and all other NASA projects and programs. NASA Headquarters is organized under the Office of The President and Vice President via the National Space Counsel. However, for federal funding authorizations, allocations, execution, and judicial matters, NASA interfaces and is bound by law to comply with elements of government: The Legislative Branch (The Congress), and the Executive Branch (The President), and the People of the United States.

Nebula – A very large volume of gas and dust that is only visible when illuminated by the radiation from stars within or nearby the nebula.

Nova – A star that experiences a cataclysmic explosion and increases its luminosity by many factors and then fades to obscurity. A Nova is a Binary star system in which one of the two stars is a White Dwarf. The White Dwarf is the source of the fantastic explosion.

O & C Building - The Operations & Checkout building located at the industrial area of the Kennedy Space Center in Florida. The O & C building is historic in that the large cleanrooms there were utilized to process the *Apollo* Spacecraft for the Lunar Missions. The same cleanrooms used in the *Apollo* Program have been converted for the Shuttle Program to process the payloads that have flown aboard the Shuttle in the cargo bay. An example is of a payload processed in those cleanrooms is the historic *Spacelab* Module.

Spacelab was a costly and complex module used to conduct experiments by Astronauts who lived and worked within the module. On specific Shuttle flights when *Spacelab* was the payload, the *Spacelab* module was connected to the Orbiter Crew Module by a tunnel. The *Spacelab* Module does not always fly on every Shuttle Mission but only when a *Spacelab* Mission is manifest. The historic *Apollo* Program's Astronaut Crew Quarters are also located in the O & C Building. Those Crew Quarters were modified in the 1970s to support the Shuttle Astronauts.

OIS System - Operational Intercom System. This systems is installed at all facilities at KSC which require space workers to be on headsets to safely and reliably conduct operations that involves many people who may also be located at various facilities at KSC and who are all in support of test, checkout, and launch procedures.

Orbit - A trajectory or path that a spacecraft or satellite follows as it circles a planet, moon, star, or other body in space. Orbits can have various elliptical or circular shapes.

Orbiter - The section of the Space Shuttle that has wings and houses the Astronauts, the payload, and Space Shuttle Main Engines. The *Orbiter* is a subsonic, transonic, supersonic, hypersonic, and ultrasonic flight vehicle, all in one. The *Orbiter* was the first reusable manned spacecraft and became the first *Spaceship*. The Orbiter has achieved thousands of documented accomplishments in aerospace engineering and sciences.

Pad - A facility that was designed for a rocket and its spacecraft payloads to be mounted for launch preparations, testing, and launch. The Pad consists of a concrete and steel pad structure, steel towers for access, and various systems support. The surrounding property contains other sub-facilities such as propellant fuel/oxidizer farms, electrical and other utility services, television, security and safety systems.

Pad A - One of the two large launch Pad facilities that support the high performance launches of the Space Shuttles. Pad A is located at the southern end of Complex 39 at the shoreline of the Kennedy Space Center.

Pad B - The second of two Space Shuttle launch Pads that is located just north of Pad A at Kennedy Space Center.

Paleontology – The study of forms of life existing in prehistoric or geologic times.

Physics – The physical science that deals with matter and energy and their transformations. Specific areas of physics are kinematics, light, sound, nuclear, electronics, particle dynamics, quantum mechanics.

Planet - A celestial body that orbits a star such as our Sun. As of the date of this copyright, only nine planets have been positively identified and photographed. All nine of those planets are in our Solar System and orbit the Sun. Although the *Hubble Space Telescope* has observed what appear to be the formations of planets far away from our Solar System, planets that are well-formed like Earth have not been photographed by Mankind at the time of this book's copyright. New space-based tele-scopes like the proposed *Extra-Terrestrial Telescope (ET)* (renamed in 2002 as the *James Webb Space Telescope*) will focus upon objects that orbit close to bright stars. The distance to the apparent early formation of a planet is so vast that our technology does not allow for our travel to that location in the Universe to study the phenomenon up close. The only known planets are, in order from the Sun, Mercury, Venus, Earth, Mars, Jupiter, Saturn, Uranus, Neptune, and Pluto.

POL -Paint/Oil Locker. A term used in industrial facilities and logistical facilities for the storage or handling of paints, oils, and other solutions and chemicals. Such facilities are located outside from a main building to reduce fire hazards to main facilities.

PRCB – Program Review Control Board

Public Health and Welfare Codes, Title-42 - The Public Law, written and approved by Congress, in which the actual charter for NASA to exist and operate is located.

Red Shift - The relationship between the position of spectral lines from the light of near and distant luminous bodies in which the greater the distance, the greater the shift toward the longer wave lengths and lower frequencies at the red end of the spectrum.

RTLS Abort - Return To Landing Site Abort. This is an emergency mode in flight that activates a particular flight software program that is designed to quickly perform functions that are essential to an immediate landing at the originating launch site. The RTLS abort maneuver can only be executed during the flight period when the ET and SRBs remain attached during boost.

Rogers Presidential Commission Report on the Challenger Accident - The official report ordered by President Reagan to investigate, not to prosecute, the *Challenger Tragedy*. The report contains recommendations to the President and to NASA as part of the Return To Flight plans after the *Challenger Tragedy*, as well as the vehicle breakup analysis and cause of death of the flight crew.

Saturn V - The three staged rocket that boosted the *Apollo Spacecraft* into Orbit around the *Moon*. The easiest way to recognize the *Saturn V* rocket is that portion of the rocket below the circular black ring at the top of the third stage, and below the *Apollo Spacecraft*.

Shuttle – A vehicle system that manages energy and work in order to transport people or cargo from one location to another.

Skylab - A very successful manned space station that orbited the Earth during most of the decade of the 1970s. Research was conducted in astrophysics, medicine, optics, astronomy, physics, electrical and aerospace engineering, geography and topography, human adaptation to space, and solar energy. Sadly, the *Skylab* was allowed to reenter the Earth's atmosphere in 1980 and left the United States without a space station.

Solid Rocket Boosters (SRBs) - The twin boosters that are attached to two sides of the *External Fuel Tank* and provide the bulk of the thrust required to lift the *Space Shuttle Orbiter* into orbit around Earth. Each of the Solid

Rocket Boosters consists of a bottom section called the Aft Skirt, four solid propellant motor segments stacked vertically, a forward cylinder section above those called the Forward Skirt, and the Frustrum and Nose Cap at the top. The Shuttle SRBs are the largest and most powerful solid rocket motors ever designed, built, flown, and above all, reused.

Soviet Union - A nation in Asia, United Soviet Socialist Republic, that had a Communist form of government. The Soviet Union had a space program that provided much of the political fuel to our American Space Program.

Space Program - All of the programs combined to equal the overall efforts of NASA.

Spaceship - A large ship where people live, work, rest, and recreate and travel. The first real *Spaceship* was the *Columbia Space Shuttle*.

Space Shuttle - The first *Spaceship* ever built and flown. A specific vehicle that was designed by NASA and its support contractor engineering companies to provide low-cost, reliable service to Low Earth Orbit for a payload not to exceed 65,000 pounds, a maximum crew of seven, and an orbital stay time of about sixteen days maximum. The Space Shuttle is a launch vehicle, living and working environment, a payload carrier, and a return to Earth vehicle, all in one design. The United States Congress authorized The Space Shuttle Design Development Test & Evaluation (DDT&E) program in 1972. The first Earth orbital flight of the Space Shuttle occurred on April 12, 1981 at Kennedy Space Center, Florida and completed forty-eight orbits in two days.

The Space Shuttle landed safely on April 14, 1981 in California on the Rogers Dry Lakebed at Edwards Air Force Base near Palmdale and Lancaster, California. The Space Shuttle consists of the Orbiter vehicle, one External Fuel Tank, and two Solid Rocket Boosters. The Space Shuttle was the first reusable hypersonic Spaceship ever flown and continues further to serve space exploration and needs for people on Earth in medical, energy, pollution solutions, astronomy, Earth Resources, and various areas of hi-tech research and development. The Space Shuttle design, operation, and missions have established thousands of world and space records in aviation, space sciences, and all other areas of the classical and nouveau sciences.

Space Shuttle Main Engines - The three engines located at the rear of the Space Shuttle Orbiter. The engines are fueled by cryogenic liquid hydrogen and oxidized by cryogenic liquid oxygen. The design of the engine employs what is called a "boot strap" system that enables the engines to pump extremely large flow rates of cryogenic propellants by developing pumping energy from functions within the engine. The SSMEs were developed from the technologies learned from the engines developed for the *Apollo* Program.

Space Station - A spaceship that is limited to a confined position or orbit. *Skylab* was the American *Space Station*. *MIR* was the Russian/former Soviet *Space Station*.

Space Telescope Science Institute (STSI) – An institute located on the campus of Johns Hopkins University in Baltimore, Maryland, that plans and operates the *Hubble Space Telescope* missions. The STSI is operated by Aura, a contractor to NASA Goddard Space Flight Center in

Greenbelt, Maryland. The scheduling, planning, and execution of the *Hubble Space Telescope* daily activities are conducted at STSI.

Star – A massive body in space that possesses extremely high levels of gravity and that is typically composed of very dense Hydrogen and Helium. The Hydrogen fuels the thermonuclear fusion reaction that ignites the star and releases profound levels of radioactive radiation that distributes energy in the local area of the star and on out farther into the Universe. The majority of the Hydrogen ultimately is converted to Helium and the star begins its powerfully demonstrative death. Stars have a birth, life, and death process that is very intriguing to scientists.

STS - The Space Transportation System, or (The Space Shuttle). This refers to *Space Shuttles,* the support equipment, facilities, funding, law, procedures, and personnel.

Sun - The proper noun that identifies the closest *star* to *planet* Earth.

Supernova – A colossal explosion of a star. There are Type I and Type II Supernovae. Type I Supernovae totally destroy the White Dwarf component of a Binary star system. Type II Supernovae are produced by the collapse of a super massive star. Supernovae are the brightest observed objects in the Universe.

The Wright Brothers - Two brothers from Dayton, Ohio named Wilbur Wright and Orville Wright who invented and patented the Flying Machine. The Wright Brothers were the first people on Earth to achieve sustained powered horizontal flight with a winged aircraft that was heavier than air. The Wright Brothers also were the inventors and test pilots for the first Practical Airplane, an airplane that would take off from a standing start, climb, level off, maintain altitude in turns, maintain aerodynamic flight control throughout all phases of flight, and land safely, immediately ready for another flight.

TPS - Thermal Protection System. The insulating system that is fundamental to the safe, reliable, reusable flights of the *Space Shuttle Orbiters.* The *TPS* System consists of three main temperature categories of insulation, low temperature, mid temperature, and high temperature. The *TPS* System is truly one of NASA and Lockheed Corporation's finest technical developments.

Truth - A particular belief or teaching regarded by the speaker as the true one. The quality of being in accordance with experience, facts, or reality. Conformity with fact. Reality; actual existence. Agreement with a standard, rule, etc.

ABOUT THE AUTHOR

Randy Avera graduated from Georgia Institute of Technology in 1977 and earned a Bachelor of Aerospace Engineering degree. The National Aeronautics and Space Administration (NASA) recruited and hired him as an Aerospace Engineer for the Space Shuttle Program at the John F. Kennedy Space Center, Florida.

From August 1977 to September 1991, while in the Shuttle Vehicle Engineering Directorate, Orbiter Mechanical Systems Division, Randy worked extensively with Orbiter structures engineering, electro-mechanical systems engineering, Shuttle Orbiter construction, launch and landing processing procedures, facility-to-Shuttle interface design, and the Orbiter window system mission requirements and maintenance procedures.

As a member of both the Launch Team and the Landing Recovery Team, Randy worked the first 39 Space Shuttle missions in his fourteen years at NASA. During that time, he was assigned to several of the special teams of the Shuttle Program. Those assignments included the *Magellan* radar mapping space probe to

Venus mission, the *Galileo* space probe to Jupiter mission, the *Long Duration Exposure Facility (LDEF)*, which was a materials experiment satellite launch and retrieval missions, the *Centaur G-Prime* Safety Study for Shuttle Interim Upper Stage Booster Development, and the *Hubble Space Telescope (HST)* mission.

Randy was a team member of the first installation of the European Space Agency/NASA *Spacelab* into the Space Shuttle Orbiter Payload Bay. Additionally, as NASA Orbiter structures engineer, he worked several years in the team effort to develop reliable repairs for damaged composite structures of the Orbiter that had been caused by overheating due to several in-flight losses of Shuttle thermal insulating tiles.

The orbiter "Zonal" and "Detailed" non-destructive testing and inspection plans were developed by the Structures Section at NASA in a large team effort to ensure safe and reliable structures for the Orbiters in the Space Shuttle fleet.

On January 29, 1986, the day after the *Challenger* Tragedy, NASA assigned Randy to the *Rogers Presidential Commission's Challenger* Crash Investigation Team to help determine the vehicle breakup sequence, which was crucial to determining the cause of the Tragedy and the fate of the crew. Space Shuttle components that Randy helped to analyze included the Orbiter *Challenger* fuselage, the Space Shuttle Main Engines (SSMEs), the Crew Module, and the 51-L Mission payload, or cargo. *The Structural Breakup Analysis Reports* and Log Sheets contained the findings of the analysis team and were submitted to the *Rogers Presidential Commission.* The team's findings are now contained in *"The Presidential Report on The Challenger Accident".* The report can be reviewed at libraries that maintain Presidential Reports, and condensed versions are available on the Internet.

At the end of 1986, Randy was assigned to conduct the functional assessment and help solve systems engineering concerns of the new egress (bail-out) system called the "The Barber Pole". This new system complemented the new "blow-away" Main Hatch System for Astronaut egress from the Orbiter that was first flown on the Shuttle *Discovery's* flight (STS-26) after the *Challenger* crash. The engineering assessment of the new crew egress system included the installation and operations development of the bailout system into the Orbiter. That system flies aboard all Space Shuttle Orbiter vehicles that have been launched by NASA beginning with STS-26.

Randy was a member of the NASA "Return-To-Flight" Team for the 26th Shuttle Transportation System flight, STS-26, Orbiter *Discovery* Mission—the first Space Shuttle flight after the *Challenger* Tragedy.

He believes in the visions of space exploration that Dr. Wernher von Braun shared; there should always be an Earth-orbiting Space Station to conduct scientific research in all areas of science. Randy believes that Human life is designed to explore the Universe and that unmanned space probes applications should be dramatically increased.

Recruited by the FAA, Aircraft Certification Office, in Atlanta, Georgia, Randy has worked since 1991 as an Aircraft Certification Engineer in that FAA office in the Aircraft Systems and Flight Test Branch. His work has included design certification and continued airworthiness engineering of commercial, private, and corporate aircraft in aircraft systems (avionics, electrical, mechanical, hydraulic, computers, and wheels and brakes). He is the designated specialist in his office for Safety Analysis of aircraft systems and operations. Randy was recognized by the FAA's aircraft inspection organization, Flight Standards Southern Region, and earned the FAA Flight Standards *"Good Friend Award 2001"* for his engineering and inspection contributions and actions that contributed highly toward preventing accidents and loss of lives in public commercial air transportation.

A model rocketry enthusiast since 1966, Randy is a member of The National High-Power Rocketry Organization, *TRIPOLI*. This organization sponsors high-power rocket developments and launches under FAA waiver requirements, Bureau of Alcohol Tobacco and Fire Arms, and the National Fire Protection Association (NFPA) guidelines.

As an FAA-certified private pilot since high school, Randy has enjoyed an extensive love and respect for his public service work and for his career in the aerospace sciences and engineering. Focused upon serving the public, Randy's career has been distinguished in serving as he says, "My flying public," and in helping the people of Earth to understand more about who we are in the Universe through exploration and science.

BOOK ORDER INFORMATION

"THE TRUTH ABOUT *Challenger*"

Randy Avera

NASA SPACE SHUTTLE ENGINEER
Challenger TRAGEDY INVESTIGATOR

BOOK ORDERS: **www.RandolphPublishing.com**
(404) 627-2468 (Office)
(404) 627-2322 (Fax)

Randolph Publishing
P.O. Box 160
Good Hope, GA 30641

UPCOMING BOOKS FROM RANDOLPH PUBLISHING:

1. "The *Fantasy* of Safe Flight", ISBN 1-932258-01-9
   Author Randy Avera
   Publish target date--October 2003
   Special Edition-(The Centennial Year of First Flight)

2. "Aliens Confirmed!", ISBN 1-932258-02-7
   A Novel.
   Author Randy Avera
   Publish target date--October 2003
   Special Edition-(The Centennial Year of First Flight)